W9-AXS-031

ADVENTURES IN LIVING PLANTS

Now we're inside the ovary.
Those round objects are the *ovules*.

EDWIN B. KURTZ, JR.
AND CHRIS ALLEN

DVENTURES IN LIVING PLANTS

THE UNIVERSITY OF ARIZONA PRESS
TUCSON, ARIZONA

Edwin B. Kurtz, Jr., Ph.D., is professor of biology at The University of Arizona.

Chris Allen, M. Ed., is an elementary school teacher in Tucson Public Schools.

Original illustrations and line drawings were done for this book by Edmund Henschel.

First printing 1965
Revised reprint 1967
Printed in the U.S.A.

Library of Congress
Card Catalog No. 64-17271

ACKNOWLEDGMENTS

A book of this type necessarily requires the skill and help of many people. We are pleased to take this opportunity to call attention to these people. Most of the writing was made possible by a sabbatical leave granted to the senior author by the University of Arizona; for this we are most grateful. Testing of the experiments was done in the second author's sixth grade classroom. We are therefore indebted to the many children who gave the text and activities the acid test. We are also most appreciative of Mr. Edmund Henschel, the artist who took our rough sketches and so skillfully created an outstanding series of original illustrations. Drs. Howard Ray and Walter S. Phillips kindly criticized the manuscript. We also owe thanks to Mrs. Darlene Anthis who typed the manuscript. We are grateful to many elementary school teachers in Tucson who experimented with various parts of this book in their classrooms and who offered advice and encouragement.

A few words of special thanks must go to Dr. G. Gamow. His stimulating and imaginative stories of the travels of Mr. Tompkins helped to create the "reducing pills" used in a number of the adventures in this book.

Photographs and certain illustrations were obtained from a number of sources. We are pleased to acknowledge them as follows:

Root system in Adv. 1: from *Principles of Plant Physiology* by James Bonner and Arthur W. Galston, adapted from Weaver and Clements, *Plant Ecology,* 2nd Ed., McGraw-Hill Book Co. San Francisco: W. H. Freeman and Company, 1952.

Photos of root tip and axillary bud, Adv. 1; photos of apical bud (external and internal views), Adv. 7; photo of lichens on pine branch, Adv. 10: Albert T. Ellis.

Photo inserts of leaf and root tip, Adv. 2; photo of albino and green corn seedlings, Adv. 9; photos of blue-green algae, *Oedogonium* egg being fertilized, brown alga along shoreline, and diatoms, Adv. 10: Robert W. Hoshaw.

Photo insert of an apical bud, Adv. 2; photos of *Spirogyra,* puffball, moss, fern plant, and fern sori, Adv. 10; photo of petrified tree logs, Adv. 11: Walter S. Phillips.

Photo of a cow with milk fever, Adv. 5: Gerald H. Stott.

Photo of penicillium on citrus fruit, Adv. 9: Rubert B. Streets.

Drawing of chromosomes of *Vicia faba,* Adv. 9: redrawn from the M.S. Thesis, University of Arizona, by Oscar G. Ward.

Electron micrograph of *Erwinia carnegiana,* Adv. 10: A. H. Gold and Stanley M. Alcorn.

Photos of a slime mold, *Rhizopus* on a tomato, cluster of mushrooms, and bracket fungi, Adv. 10: Paul D. Keener.

Photo of tree-rings, Adv. 10: Tree-Ring Laboratory, University of Arizona, courtesy of W. McGinnies.

Photo of mammoth diorama, Adv. 11: Arizona State Museum, courtesy of Emil Haury.

Photos of vegetational change in southern Arizona, Adv. 11: U.S. Forest Service, courtesy of Clark Martin.

Finally, we wish to thank the staff of the University of Arizona Press for all their patience, help, and understanding.

Edwin B. Kurtz, Jr.
Chris Allen

This book is dedicated to

Gary
Janie
Kathy
and Pam

CONTENTS

ADVENTURE 1

A Map Of Our Adventures

THE PLANT BODY

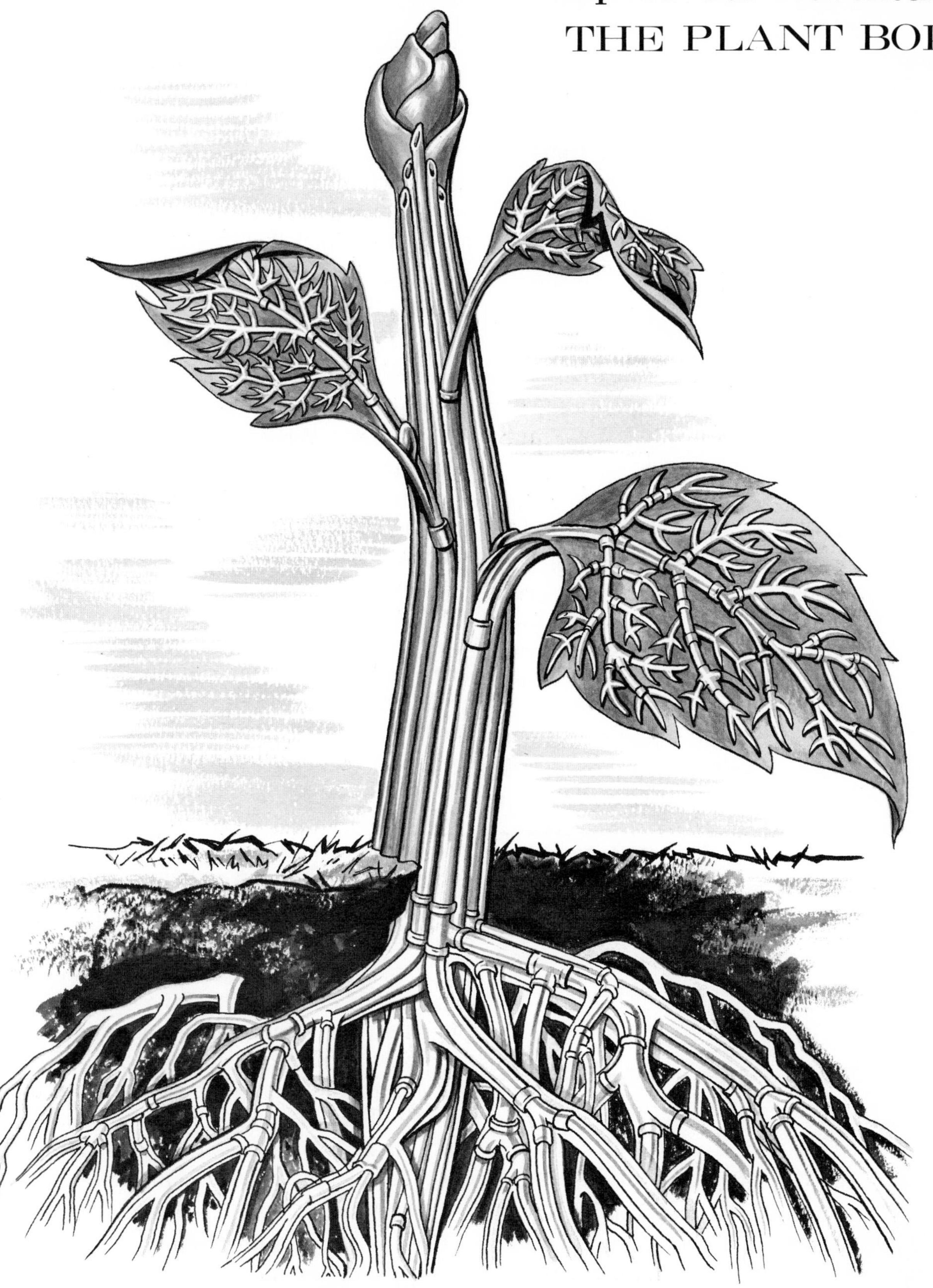

Plants have a "plumbing system." Water and food flow in these pipes.

A Map Of Our Adventures

WOULD you like to go on some trips? I don't mean ordinary trips by car or train or plane. I mean special trips that are big adventures! The adventures I'm talking about aren't for softies, though. Do you still want to go? Good! I had hoped you would. Before we go on our first trip I think I should tell you a few things about plants. Then you will enjoy the thrills of the trip a lot more.

First, how many different kinds of plants do you think there are? A few thousand? Ten thousand? One hundred thousand? Well, about five hundred thousand (500,000) kinds have been found and named so far! More are being found each year. The kinds of plants that you see most often are those that form flowers: grasses, oak trees, cacti, corn. Most of the plants that you eat are plants that form flowers. Think for a moment; how many more kinds of plants that have flowers do you know? What about those that don't form flowers? How many of these do you know? I'll name a few kinds of plants and you find the ones that have flowers:

Lettuce
Pine trees
Mushrooms and other molds
Green scum in pond water
Helpful bacteria and germs that cause disease
Carrots
Ferns
Watermelons
Spinach
Roses

How many did you find? Five? Did you find lettuce, carrots, watermelons, spinach, and roses? All of these plants form flowers; and their flowers form seeds. Mushrooms, molds, green scum (algae) in pond water, bacteria, and ferns do not have flowers and do not form seeds. What about pine trees? You're right; they form seeds, but the seeds are formed inside cones rather than flowers!

Most of our adventures in this book will be with plants that form flowers; but we will do a little exploring also of plants that don't form flowers.

Let's take a closer look at plants that have flowers. What other parts do they all have besides flowers? Look around you at plants growing in your yard, in pots inside your home, in the school yard, or wherever you are. What do you see? Do they all have branches? Do they all have leaves? If it is winter time where you are living, you may not see leaves on some plants. Do you know why? The branches of a plant are called stems; they hold a plant up in the air. Attached around the stems are leaves. Do you know what is attached to the bottom end of the stem? That's right, roots. If you haven't seen roots, pull up some small weeds and look at their roots. You will see living roots in action in some of the experiments at the end of this adventure.

Some roots grow straight down into the ground. They are *tap roots*. Dandelions have tap roots. Can you guess why it is so hard to get rid of dandelions in your lawn by digging them up? Some plants have tap roots that go 30 to 50 feet down into the soil! Roots that are not tap roots go in all directions into the soil. They are called *fibrous roots*. Most grass plants have fibrous roots. The roots of most plants grow only in the top two or three feet of soil.

How many roots do you think a plant has? If you put all the roots of a plant end-to-end, how long would the row of roots be? It isn't

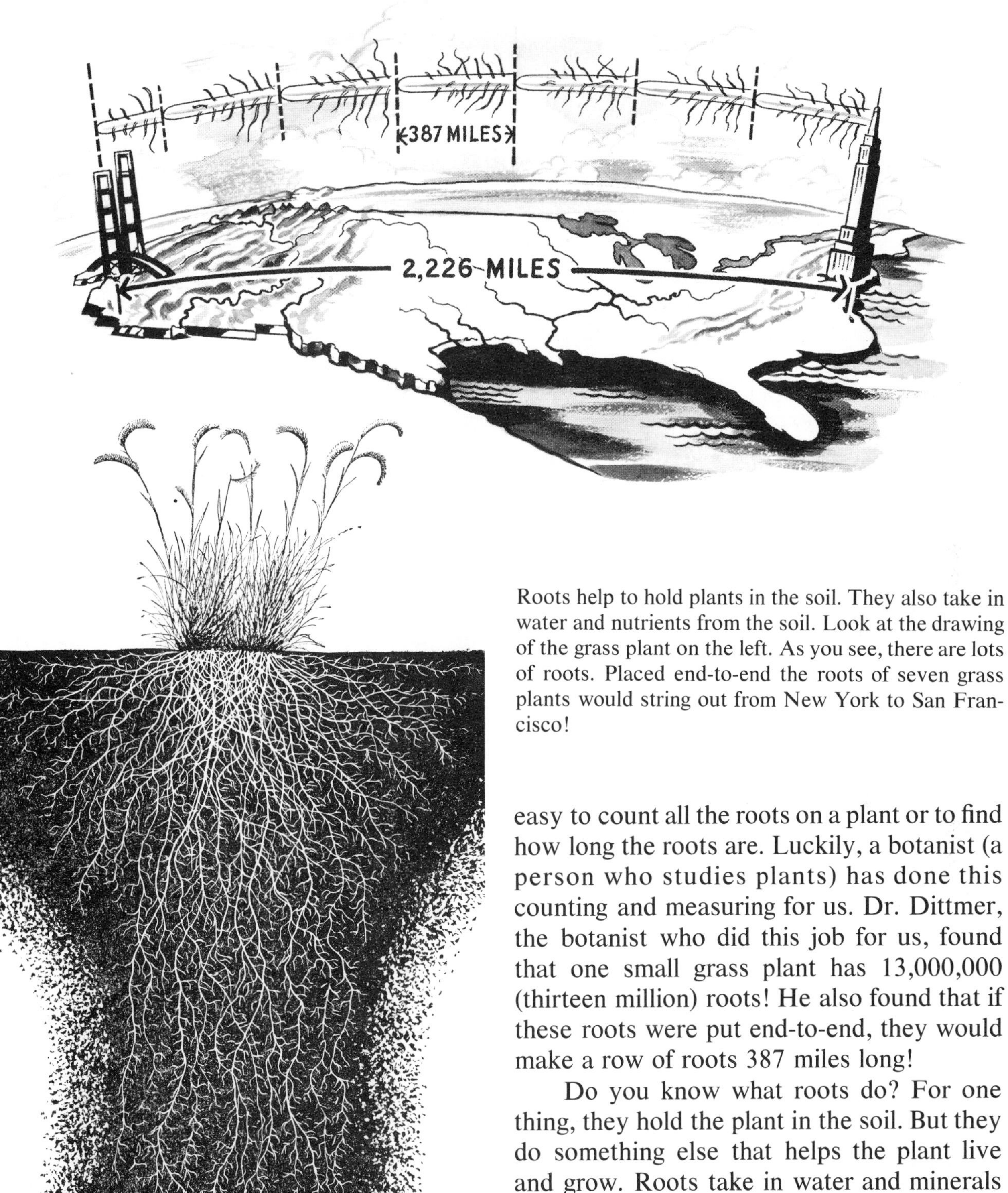

Roots help to hold plants in the soil. They also take in water and nutrients from the soil. Look at the drawing of the grass plant on the left. As you see, there are lots of roots. Placed end-to-end the roots of seven grass plants would string out from New York to San Francisco!

easy to count all the roots on a plant or to find how long the roots are. Luckily, a botanist (a person who studies plants) has done this counting and measuring for us. Dr. Dittmer, the botanist who did this job for us, found that one small grass plant has 13,000,000 (thirteen million) roots! He also found that if these roots were put end-to-end, they would make a row of roots 387 miles long!

Do you know what roots do? For one thing, they hold the plant in the soil. But they do something else that helps the plant live and grow. Roots take in water and minerals from the soil. The roots and the other parts of the plant need the water and minerals to grow and live. If all the roots of a plant were flattened out, they would cover the floor of a basketball court! Now can you see how the millions and millions of roots help a plant to take in water and minerals?

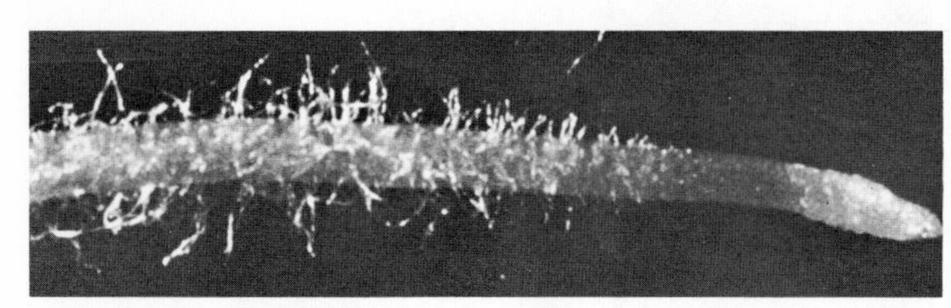

Helping the roots to take in water are literally billions of small, fuzzy root hairs. Each one is a single cell.

Roots also have *root hairs*. They are formed near the tip of a root. Each root hair is a single cell and looks like a small white hair. Root hairs help each root to take in water. Since there are millions of hairs on the roots of a plant, they can be a lot of help. One of our adventures will be a trip inside root hairs and roots. I know you will like it.

Next time you look at a plant, think of the millions of roots that are growing down in the ground. Think of the millions of fuzzy root hairs. Think of the hundreds of miles of roots twisting through the soil. Think of all these roots and root hairs taking in water and minerals from the soil. The roots of a plant are like a long, stringy, living sponge!

Now let's look at what is attached to the top of the roots: the stem. The stem is filled with plumbing pipes! Water and minerals from the roots flow in these pipes to the leaves, flowers and fruits. The pipes also carry food from old leaves to young leaves, flowers, fruits, roots, and other plant parts that need food. We will go on an exciting trip through the plumbing pipes of plants in a later adventure!

Attached to the stems are leaves. There are many shapes and sizes of leaves. Think of the different kinds you have seen: round, narrow, hairy, thick, thin, large, small. Most leaves are green. Can you think of any plants whose leaves are not green?

Some leaves have only a flat part called a *leaf blade*. Other leaves have a leaf blade and a small stalk that connects the blade to the stem. This stalk is called a *petiole*. The petioles have the same kinds of plumbing pipes inside them as are inside the stem. In fact, the plumbing pipes in the petiole connect to the pipes in the stem. After the plumbing pipes pass through the petiole, they spread into a leaf blade. The pipes in the leaf blade are called *veins*. Look at the leaves on some living plants. Can you find the leaf blade? Does the leaf you are looking at have a petiole? Can you find some plants that have leaves without petioles? Do you see veins in the leaves?

Now we know what roots, stems, and leaves are, but where do they come from? How are they formed? Have you seen the tiny plant inside a seed? This young plant has a root, a small stem, and one or two tiny leaves. When you plant a seed, the tiny plant starts to grow and get bigger. First the root pops out of the seed and goes into the soil. Then the stem and leaves come out of the seed and grow up into the air above the soil. A seedling is a marvelous thing, and there are many things we would like to know about it. How did the small, young plant get inside the seed? Have you ever wondered why roots always grow down into the soil? Why do stems always grow up into the air? Why don't we see roots growing up into the air just once in a while? How does the plant grow larger? A living plant does many marvelous things that we will want to find out about.

We said that the tiny plant inside a seed has one root and one stem. Then where do all the millions of roots on a plant come from? And many plants have more than one stem. Where do these stems come from? And where do all the leaves and flowers come from? Let's see! Let's watch a seedling as it grows.

Here comes the first root of the tiny plant inside the seed. A second root is forming inside the first root. As the first root grows, the second root also grows. It grows, and grows until it gets large enough to poke out the side of the first root. Here it comes! Now the second root has some roots growing inside it, too. Each root makes new roots. If we watched this plant for a few days or weeks, we would see millions of roots formed. Roots will grow in all directions in the soil; yet they all lead back to the first root. The roots of a plant are like the driveway and streets near your home. Pretend that the driveway to your house is the first root. Attached to your driveway is a street which soon comes to another street. The second street runs into other streets. The other streets run into still more streets. There are many streets, but they all connect back to your driveway.

Where do stems come from? We said that the first stem is part of the tiny plant inside a seed. The top of this small stem is called a *bud*. As the bud grows it makes the first stem longer. This bud also forms other buds along the side of the stem. Each bud on the side of the stem grows into a stem which forms its own buds. So stems form buds which grow into new stems; and these new stems form more buds. Look at some young branches of trees or some plants in a flower garden; you will see the two kinds of buds: a bud at the tip of the stem and buds along the side of the stem.

Where do leaves come from? The first leaves are found inside the seed. Where do the other leaves on a plant come from? Buds! Yes, the same buds that make stems also make

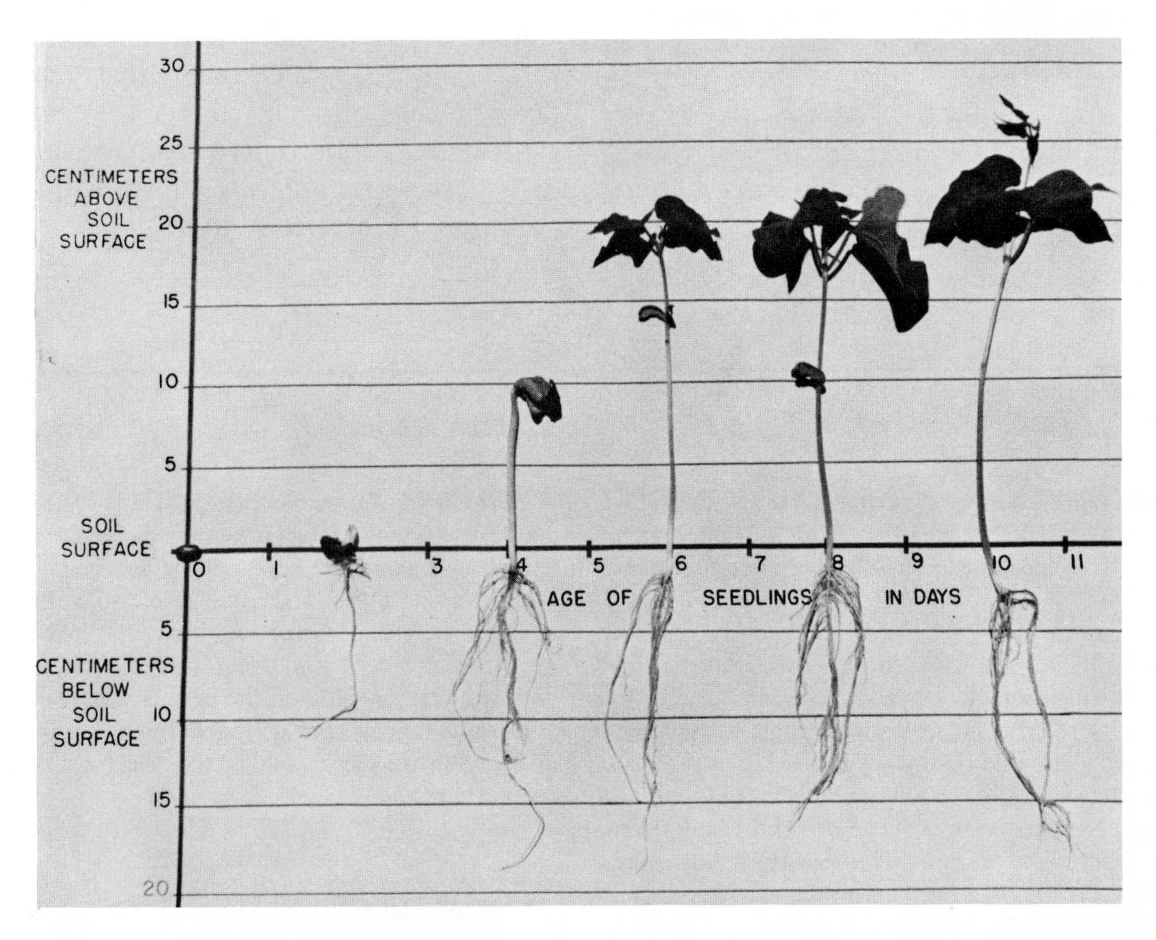

You can see at a glance that the height and depth below the soil of these little seedlings are dependent upon their varying ages. Could you plan an experiment so all plants would be ready for a picture at the same time?

This bud is attached to the plant where the leaf joins the stem. Tiny leaves are inside this bud.

leaves. As a bud grows and forms a longer stem, it also forms leaves. The leaves are attached to the side of the stem. Find a bud at the top of a stem and look at it closely. Do you see all the tiny leaves inside the bud? These tiny leaves will grow into large leaves in a few days.

Where do flowers come from? Actually, flowers are special leaves that do special things. We will learn about that later when we take a trip through a flower. But right now we want to know where flowers come from. Well, since leaves come from buds, and flowers are special leaves, can you guess where flowers come from? That's right; they come from buds!

Now we have looked at all the parts of the plant body. We have seen its roots, stems, leaves and flowers. We have also found where these parts come from. Later we will explore what goes on inside each of these parts. Plants do not sleep, jump, talk, or think, as you and I do. But plants are alive and do many curious things. They do some things that you and I do. They also do many things we cannot do, such as make food. There are many things for us to discover in our adventures with plants! And now we are ready to begin!

Things to Do and Think About

BEFORE you start on an experiment, read it slowly first. Then you will know what it is about. Then you will also know what things you will need to do the experiment. Get all the supplies together before you start.

1. Buds for science and eating. Get one or more of the following: complete bunch of celery, head of lettuce, head of cabbage, onion bulb. Start with the outside leaves and one-by-one, peel them away from the rest of the vegetable. You may need a magnifying glass to see the small leaves in the center of the bud. Count the number of leaves you find in each vegetable. What does the growing tip (at the very center) of the stem look like? What part or parts of a plant is a bunch of celery? A head of lettuce? A head of cabbage? An onion bulb?

2. Parts of seedlings. Get several kinds of seeds: radish seeds, tomato seeds, grass seeds (really they are fruits!) and sunflower seeds (these are fruits, too!). If you can't find these, find some other kinds. Put 3 or 4 layers of newspapers or paper towels in the bottom of a pie pan or other large, flat container. Soak the paper with water; then pour off the excess water. Put about 10 of each kind of seed on the wet paper. Finally set a dish or lid over the pie pan so that there are no cracks around the edge.

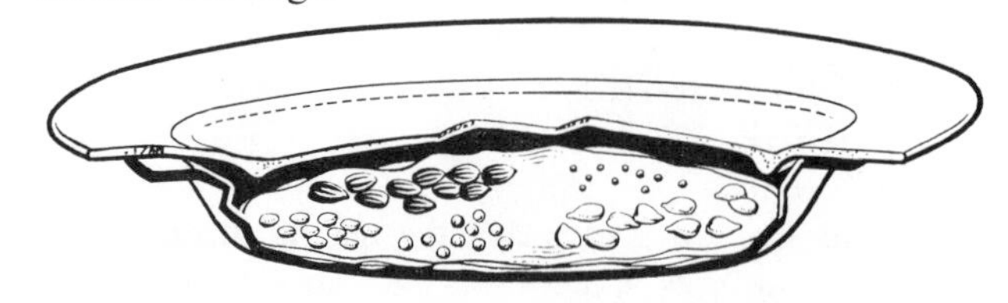

Put the germination set-up in a warm place, but not in direct sunlight or on top of a radiator. Look at the seeds every day. See what the seedlings look like as the seeds germinate. You may have to sprinkle some water on the paper to keep it wet. Be careful not to flood the seeds, though (Why?).

What part of the seed comes out first? How many embryo leaves come out of each kind of seed? Do leaves grow out of all kinds of seeds? Look at the root tip and root hairs with a magnifying glass. How many root hairs are there on each root? About how long are the root hairs? Are most of the root hairs on a root near the root tip? Can you see the plumbing pipes inside the root? What color are the seedlings you have grown?

You may want to plant some of the seedlings in soil. Then you can watch them grow into mature plants. Use waxed paper drinking cups from a soda fountain for pots. With a nail, punch one hole in the bottom of each cup. Fill the cup to about 2 inches from the top with loose, sandy soil. Then carefully hold a seedling over the soil in the cup; pour more soil around the roots of the seedling until the roots have been covered. Slowly water the soil. Don't put the potted plants in direct sunlight until a couple days later (Why?). With a little practice you will be able to get most of the seedlings you transplant to grow into healthy plants.

3. Roots, roots, and more roots. Carefully dig up (do not pull up) a small weed, grass, or other plant. Put the root system and soil into a bucket of water. Very *slowly* and *carefully* wash the soil away from the roots. Try not to break any roots. Rinse the roots several times in fresh water (not running water) until they are as clean as you can get them. Save the stems and leaves. Now do these things:

a) Count the number of main roots.
b) How many side roots does each main root have?
c) Knowing "a" and "b" calculate the total number of roots the plant has.
d) How long are the main roots?
e) How long are the side roots of a main root?
f) Can you calculate the total length of all the roots on this plant?
g) Compare the total length of roots to the total length of stems on this plant.
h) Compare the weight of roots to the weight of stems and leaves of this plant. If you don't have a balance, do this by holding all the roots in one hand and all the stems and leaves in the other hand. Which hand feels heavier?

4. What are leaves and stems? Get the leaves and stems from several kinds of plants. Look at them closely. Make a list of all the different characteristics of these leaves and stems you can see. For example, do all the leaves have petioles? Are all the leaves the same shape? Also make a list of the characteristics that all the leaves or stems have. For example, are all the leaves green or partly green? After looking at all these likenesses and differences, could you explain to someone what a leaf looks like? Could you explain what a stem looks like?

5. Making some buds, roots, stems, and leaves. You will need one fresh onion bulb and one potato; two glasses or jars with mouths about 3 inches in diameter; 6 strong toothpicks or 6 nails as long as toothpicks.

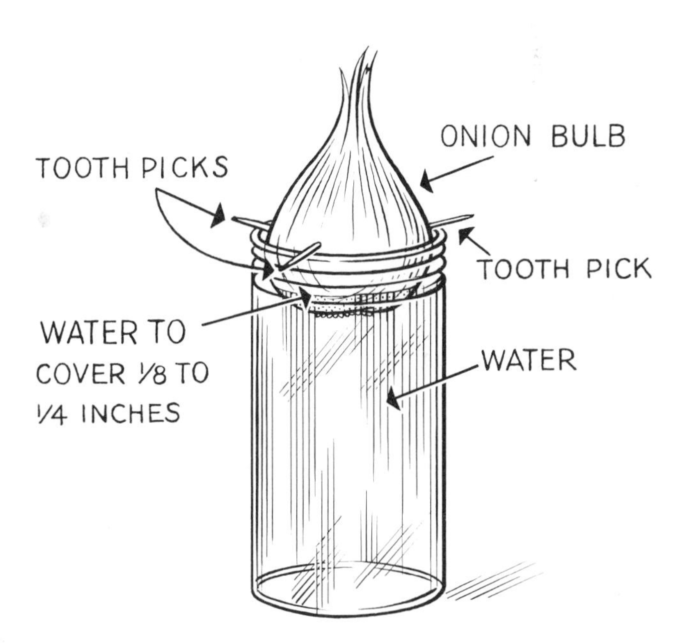

Carefully stick 3 of the toothpicks or nails into the onion like they are in the drawing. Now pour enough water into the glass or jar so that the bottom of the onion dips into the water. The onion should dip into the water about one-half inch. Place the onion set-up in a dark cabinet or closet; be sure the closet isn't cold and that the water won't be spilled.

Now look at the potato. A potato is a special kind of stem; do the "eyes" of the potato look like buds? Let's see if the potato eyes are buds! Find the end of the potato which has the most eyes; this is the top end of the stem. Hold the top end up; now stick 3 toothpicks or nails into the potato just like you did with the onion. Set the potato over a glass or jar. Pour in water until the bottom end of the potato dips into the water one-fourth to one-half inch. Place this potato set-up in the dark closet or cabinet next to the onion set-up.

Look at the onion and potato every day. Watch for new roots, leaves, and stems. Also check each day to see if the bottom end of the onion and potato are still dipping into the water. Add enough water each day to keep the bottom ends covered.

Look at the onion and potato each day for at least two weeks; longer if you want to. See what you find out on these points:

1. Where roots grow from?
2. What do some of the potato eyes do?
3. Are potato eyes buds?
4. Do any of the roots have root hairs?
5. Do any of the roots branch and form side roots?
6. Are the leaves and stems green?
   At the end of your experiment, move the onion set-up and potato set-up into a bright room; do not put them in direct sunlight, though. Watch what happens during the next few days. Discover what happens to the size and color of the leaves and stems.
7. Do the onion bulb and potato get shriveled? Do you know why?

6. *Look at a plant.* See if you can find each of these parts:

fruit	root	petiole
seed	leaf	veins
stem tip and bud	flower	hairs
stem	root hair	buds that will grow
root tip	leaf blade	into side branches

ADVENTURE 2
The Building Blocks Of Plants
CELLS

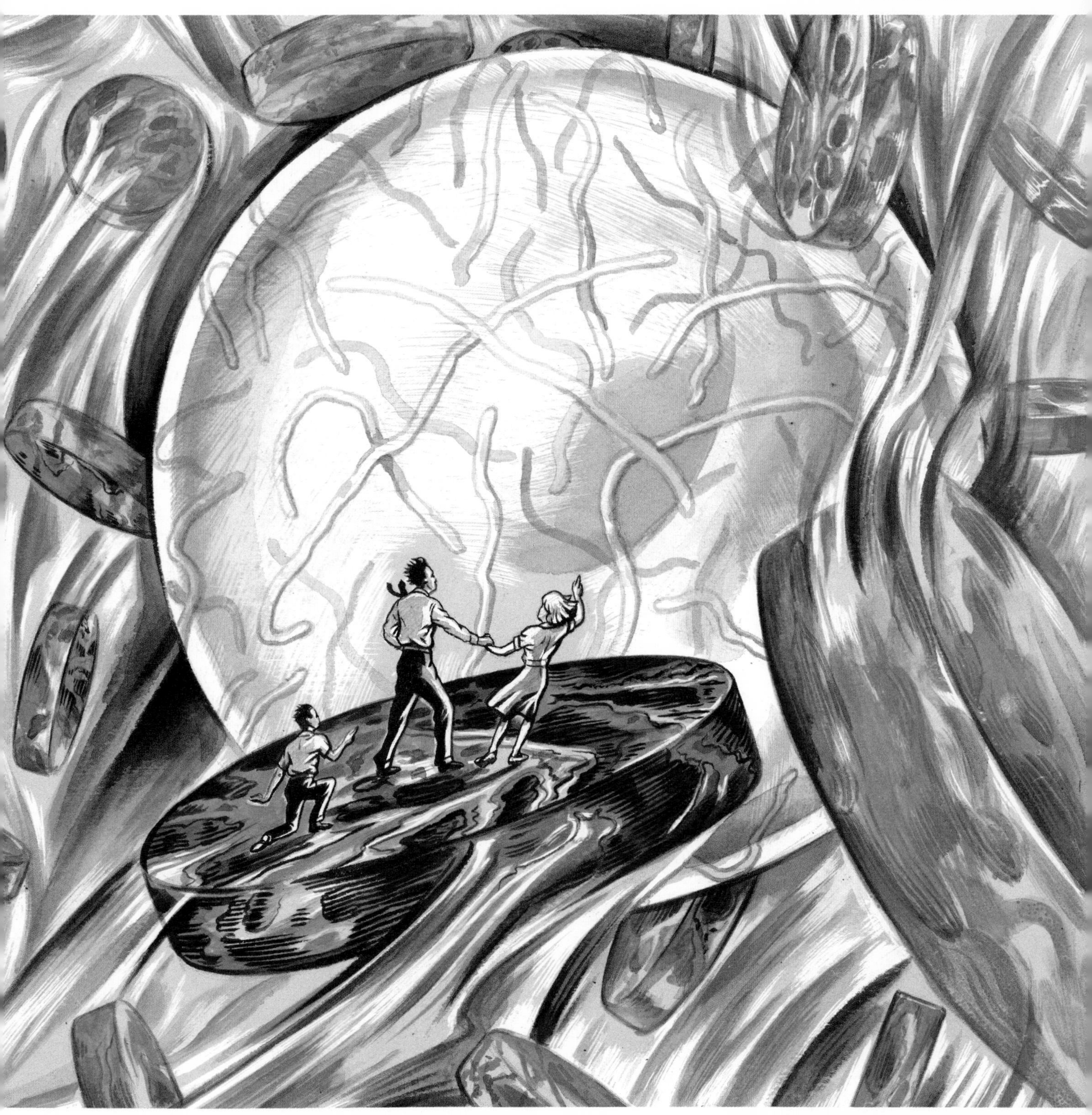

As we ride this chloroplast around the plant cell, we can see the "brains" or *nucleus*. Those twisted, stringy things inside the nucleus are *chromosomes*.

THINK of all the parts of plants that you can: leaves, stems, roots, flowers, buds, seeds, fruits, hairs, thorns. As different as these parts are, all of them are made of cells. Each cell is like a brick in a building. When bricks are cemented together in various ways, different buildings are made. When cells are glued together in various ways, different parts of plants are formed. You have seen many sizes, shapes, and colors of bricks. There are also many sizes, shapes, and colors of cells to build plants with.

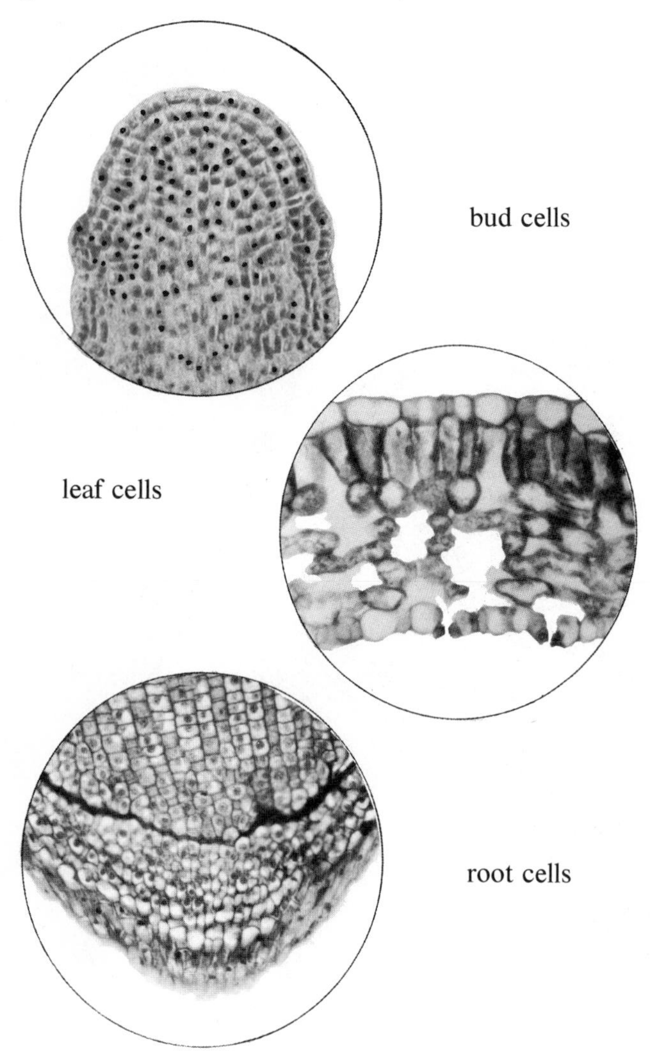

bud cells

leaf cells

root cells

But no matter what cell we talk about, they are all about the same; nearly all cells have the same kinds of parts inside. Let's go on a trip to the inside of a plant cell and see what these parts look like! Your body is about one million times larger than plant cells, so you will have to swallow this special reducing pill.* It will make you small enough to fit inside a cell! The effect of the pill wears off after half an hour, so don't worry about staying microscopic all your life! We will want to use these reducing pills on other adventures into plants and cells, so don't be afraid to swallow it. You don't want to miss all the fun and excitement of these adventures inside plants!

Are you ready? Let's visit the green cells in the leaves of grass in your front yard. Take my hand! Now, swallow the pill. There goes mine. And now yours. Don't be frightened. I've made this trip many times. Just hold on to my hand so we won't get lost! Since we were standing on your front yard on some grass, we won't have any trouble finding some grass cells to. . . . go. . . . . in. . . . . . . toooooo. . . oo. . . o. . . . .

Ah, here we are now. You are now one millionth as tall as you were a few seconds ago! Didn't hurt a bit, did it? This wide flat thing we are standing on is a grass leaf. Watch out! You almost fell in one of those big holes in the leaf surface! Molecules of gases go in and out of the leaf through those holes. The holes are called *stomates.* See that swarm of

*I want to thank Mr. Tompkins and Dr. G. Gamow for their help in discovering the chemical formula of these special reducing pills.

Wow! Look at those small, flea-like bodies swarming out of that big hole! Those are *molecules* of gas coming out of the leaf. They are coming up through the *stomate,* an opening in the surface of the leaf.

small flea-like bodies coming out of that stomate? They are molecules of oxygen and water coming out of the leaf. But let's not bother with them. We came here to see some cells! Be careful now, and hold my hand. We are going to slide down the side of one of these large holes. Then we will be inside the leaf where the cells are. Hold on. Here we go!

I forgot to ask you if you can swim. Glad to see that you can, because the water gets rather deep at times inside the leaf. Each cell has a coating of water over it, and it may get over our heads as we walk along the surface of the cells. See how bright it is inside the leaf? We can see our way easily because sunlight shines through the leaf. But be careful where you walk! You may slide over the edge of the cell we're standing on and get hurt from the fall! Because you are reduced in size, a fall off this cell would be like falling off a tall building!

Now let's go into the cell we're standing on. If we look around, we'll find a place in the wall of the cell that is thin. A cell is like a box with watery juice and other things inside the box. But the wall of the box has some thin spots where we can break through. Here's one! See how the *cell wall* is made of many threads? The wall is like a piece of cloth, except the threads are criss-crossed in all directions. Help me push these threads aside so that we can slip through the wall and enter the cell. Thanks! Now let's enter the cell. But watch out; things move fast in the cell and you may get hit by flying objects. The juice of the cell moves fast too, and you may get swept downstream. Hang onto my hand; I don't want to lose you!

Quick! Jump onto this large green disk coming toward us! There will be just enough room for all of us to sit on it. This is much better. Now we can relax and ride this green disk around the cell just as we would ride in a car around town. The green disk we are sitting on is a *chloroplast*. That means a "green body." Molecules of green *chlorophyll* inside this chloroplast make it this green color. You can see the chlorophyll molecules underneath where you are sitting. A chloroplast is a food-factory because food is made in it. We'll explore that on another trip.

Look out! Sorry I had to push your head down; another chloroplast just came floating by and nearly hit you! I can see about 50 chloroplasts in this cell, so watch out! They are all moving. You are probably wondering what makes all these chloroplasts and the watery juice move inside the cell. Well, I wonder, too! No one has found what makes the things inside a cell move about, but they do. Of course, when this cell gets old the juice won't move as fast as it does now. And when this cell dies, all the juice, chloroplasts, and other things will dry up. The box around the cell (the cell wall) will be left, though.

Hang on tight; the chloroplast we're sitting on is going to swing around the end of the cell and the trip may get bumpy! Well, that wasn't as bumpy as I had expected! See that large jelly-like glob we now are passing? It is the "brains" of the cell. It is the *nucleus*. Can you see all those twisted stringy things inside the nucleus? Those are *chromosomes*. You have probably heard of the Morse Code. Well, the different molecules that each chromosome is made of are arranged in special ways to make a code. This special arrangement of the molecules is like a secret code. One molecule is like a "dot," another is like a "dash." Thousands of the molecules are arranged to form many "dots" and "dashes." This code tells the cell what things it has to do, and also tells the cell how to do them. The arrangement of molecules in chromosomes tells the cell how to make chlorophyll, how to make a cell wall, and how to do all the thousands of things a cell has to do to be alive. Of course, the code is much more complex than merely "dots" and "dashes." In fact, it is so complex that no one has found out how it works! We will take a trip into a nucleus later. Then I can show you more about how the nucleus works. By the way, every cell of your body has a nucleus. And each nucleus contains twisted chromosomes, too. But your chromosomes don't tell you to make chlorophyll! If they did, you would be colored green!

We've just about traveled all the way through the juice of a cell. I believe I forgot to tell you what the juice is called. It is *cytoplasm,* which means cell juice. Most of the cytoplasm is water. But many things are mixed in with the water. See those flea-like objects in the cytoplasm? Some of them are molecules of oxygen (O_2) and carbon dioxide (CO_2) gas. See the slightly larger objects, the ones that move like flies? They are molecules of sugar and other foods. And do you see all those things that look like long, twisted, licorice sticks? They are *enzyme* molecules. There are thousands of different kinds of enzymes in the cytoplasm of this cell. Each kind of enzyme has a different job to do. Some enzymes break sugars into small pieces; other enzymes make fats; still others make starch, or chlorophyll, or cell walls. Enzymes are the machinery of the cell. But we can talk about enzymes another time. The effect of the special reducing pill will wear off in another minute; we had better take a last look at the stuff inside this cell before we have to leave!

As we sit on top of this chloroplast and move around the inside of the cell, we can see many things. We see about 50 green chloroplasts moving through the cytoplasm; we can see the jelly-like nucleus containing chromosomes; and we can see billions of molecules of gases, sugars, food, and enzymes swarming through the cytoplasm. But we passed up one important part of the cell. That is the *vacuole*.

Take a quick look at it before we leave. See it over there, that big bag toward the center of the cell? The vacuole is like a balloon filled with water and put in the middle of the cell. The vacuole doesn't contain enzymes or chloroplasts; it really is like a big tank of water. The water helps keep the cell from drying up.

Whoops! I see our time has just about run out. I'll draw a picture of a cell for you when we get back to normal size. When the effect of the reducing pill wears off, you will suddenly get one million times larger than you are now. Then you will be back to normal size! As we get larger we will burst out of this cell. We will be standing on the grass in your front yard, right where we started 30 minutes ago! Sooooo lo . . . o . . . n . . . . g . . . . .

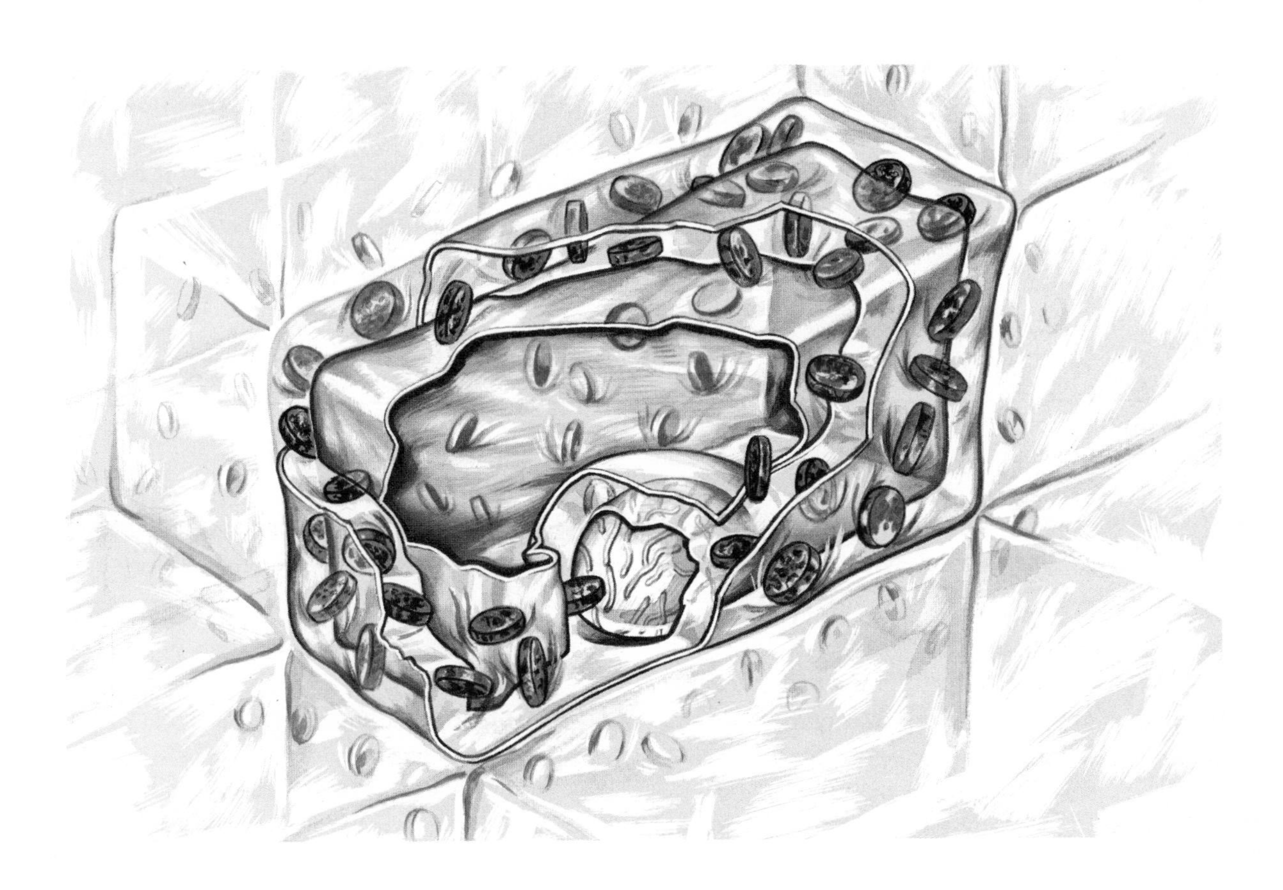

Here's the drawing of a cell I promised you. Part of the cell wall was left out so you can see inside the cell better. Can you find the *nucleus*? The watery bag in the center is the *vacuole*. The juice between the vacuole and the cell wall is *cytoplasm*.

Things to Do and Think About

1. Some views of cells. You will need a piece of cork or soft wood, a sharp knife, and a magnifying glass. Carefully slice a very thin piece from the end of the cork or wood. The thin piece should be so thin you can almost see through it. Hold the thin section up to the light and look at it with a magnifying glass.

Can you see the cell walls? Are all the cells the same size? Try cutting a thin piece from the side of the cork or wood. Do the cells look the same as in the first section? Try drawing a picture to show the shape of the cells you have seen.

Make some very thin sections or slices of other plants: small stems, a stalk of celery, balsa wood, pine needles, etc. Examine these and see what sizes and shapes of cells you can find. If you have a microscope, use it to examine the slices. Lay the slice on a microscope slide, cover the slice with a drop of water, and put a cover glass over the water drop before you look at it through the microscope.

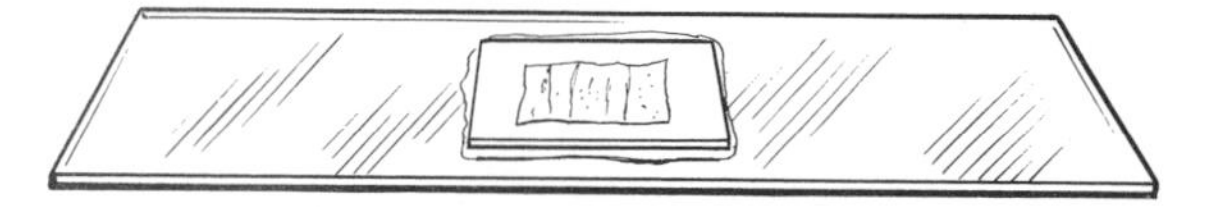

2. What are cells made of? Go to the grocery store and buy a head of lettuce, a large potato, or some large fleshy vegetable. Weigh the vegetable at the grocery store and record the weight. Take the vegetable home and cut it into many thin slices and shredded pieces. Do this cutting over a pie pan so that the plant juice will not be lost. Spread the slices of the vegetable over the pan so that they can dry out. Put the pan and the slices in the sunlight, or over a radiator, or some place where they can dry fast without being burned. Turn the slices over, every now and then; this will speed up the drying. After the vegetable is as dry as it will get, ask your mother to let you put the pan and slices in the oven of her stove. Use a very low heat (about 200°F.) for about 2 hours. Be careful not to burn or char them! Now the plant should be completely dry.

When the vegetable is completely dry, scrape the dry material into a sack or dry bottle. Take it to the grocery store and reweigh the dry vegetable. Record the weight.

After you have obtained the weight of the dry vegetable, return home with the dry matter. Put the dry matter in a pile in the center of a heavy iron skillet (check with your mother to make sure you have her permission to do this). Then put the skillet on the stove and heat it. First put it on low heat, then on medium heat, and finally on high heat. Try not to let the dry material catch fire; just make it smolder and char. After it has stopped smoldering, turn off the stove and let the skillet cool to room temperature.

When the skillet is cool, scrape the ashes into an envelope. Then determine the weight of the ashes on scale at the grocery store or on a sensitive balance at school. Pour the ashes onto a sheet of paper when you weigh them. Be careful not to mess up the balance with the ashes.

Record your weighings in the following table. Then see if you can do the calculations:

1. Name of vegetable used ____________
2. Weight of fresh vegetable ____________
3. Weight of dry vegetable ____________
4. Weight of water lost ____________
   (item 2 minus item 3)
5. Weight of ashes ____________
6. Weight of food burned away ____________
   (item 3 minus item 5)
7. % Weight of water in fresh vegetable ______%
   (divide item 4 by item 2 and then multiply by 100)
8. % Weight of dry matter in fresh vegetable ______%
   (divide item 3 by item 2 and then multiply by 100)
9. % Weight of ashes in fresh vegetable ______%
   (divide item 5 by item 2 and then multiply by 100)

10. % Weight of food in fresh vegetable ______%
(divide item 6 by item 2 and then multiply by 100)

What does a vegetable contain the most of? What chemicals are in the dry matter of a vegetable? In the fresh vegetable, what parts of cells contained the water? Where is the dry matter in the cells of the vegetable? Where did the living vegetable get the chemicals that are in the ashes? Were any of these chemicals in the seed that grew into the plant and vegetable?

3. Looking at cells through a microscope. You will need a low power microscope and an onion bulb for this experiment. Cut a fresh, juicy onion leaf away from an onion bulb. Carefully peel off the inner skin (the skin on the side of the leaf that was toward the center of the onion bulb). Quickly place a piece of this skin in a drop of water on a microscope slide. Lay a cover slip over the skin and look at it through the microscope. You may have to adjust the light and mirror so that the light is not too bright.

Can you find the parts of the cells? Can you see the cell wall, cytoplasm, and nucleus? The nucleus looks like a small blob of jelly and is about one-tenth as long as the cell. Are there any chloroplasts in the cells of the onion bulb skin?

Try the same experiment with small leaves from plants growing in an aquarium. If you don't have an aquarium, you can get a couple of small plants at a pet or variety store that sells aquarium supplies; they cost about a dime. Can you find chloroplasts in the cells of these water plants?

If you live near a stream, irrigation ditch, sea shore, lake, or pond that has some green scum (algae) in it, look at some of this scum through a microscope. Mount the scum on a slide in a little water, and cover it with a cover slip. You will be able to see many shapes and sizes of cells. Do any of the cells move?

4. How many cells are in a tree? Most cells are so small that their size cannot be measured in inches or centimeters. They are usually measured in microns. A micron is a unit of length: one micron is 1/10,000 of a centimeter, or 1/25,400 of an inch. In other words, there are 25,400 microns in an inch.

There are many sizes of cells; an average cell is 50 microns long, 10 microns wide, and 10 microns high.

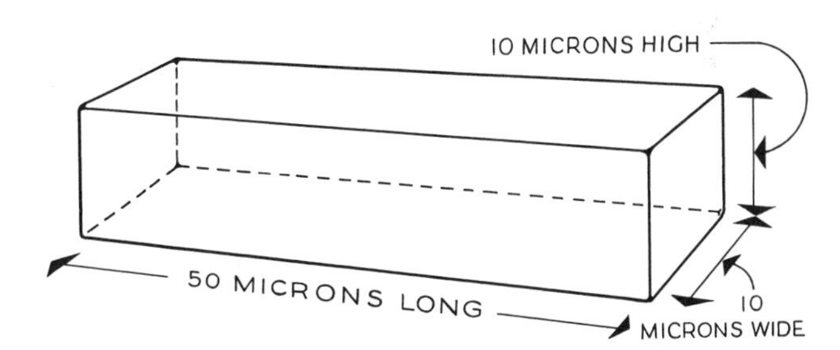

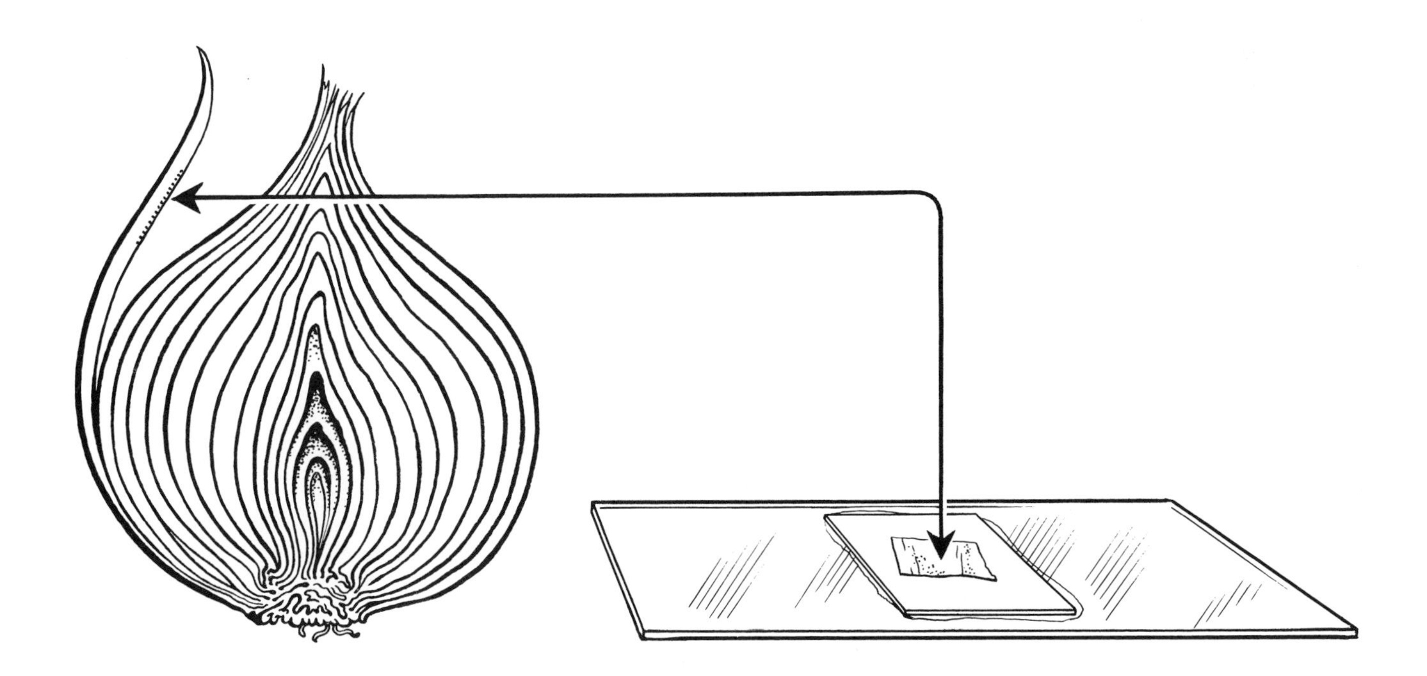

You can get a good look at a cell by placing a thin piece of onion skin on a slide, under a microscope.

Use the length, width, and height of this average cell to figure out the following things. You will be amazed at what you find!

a. How many average cells would have to be laid end-to-end to make a row of cells one inch long?
b. What is the volume of an average cell in cubic microns?
c. What is the area (in square microns) of each side and end of this average cell?
d. What is the total area (in square microns) of all the sides and ends of this average cell?
e. How many of these average cells could be packed into a box that is 1 inch high, 1 inch wide, and 1 inch long?
f. An average tree contains about 100 cubic feet of cells. If all the cells in this tree were 50 x 10 x 10 microns in size, how many cells would be in the tree?

(Hint: a cubic foot is 12 inches long, 12 inches high, and 12 inches wide.)

Check your answers below.

Answers to problems a-f:

a. 508 cells.
b. 5000 cubic microns.
c. The sides are each 500 square microns; the ends are each 100 square microns.
d. The total area is 2200 square microns.
e. About 3,300,000,000 cells.
f. There would be about 570,000,000,000,000 cells in the tree. That's 570 trillion cells!

ADVENTURE 3

Food-Making By Green Plants

PHOTOSYNTHESIS

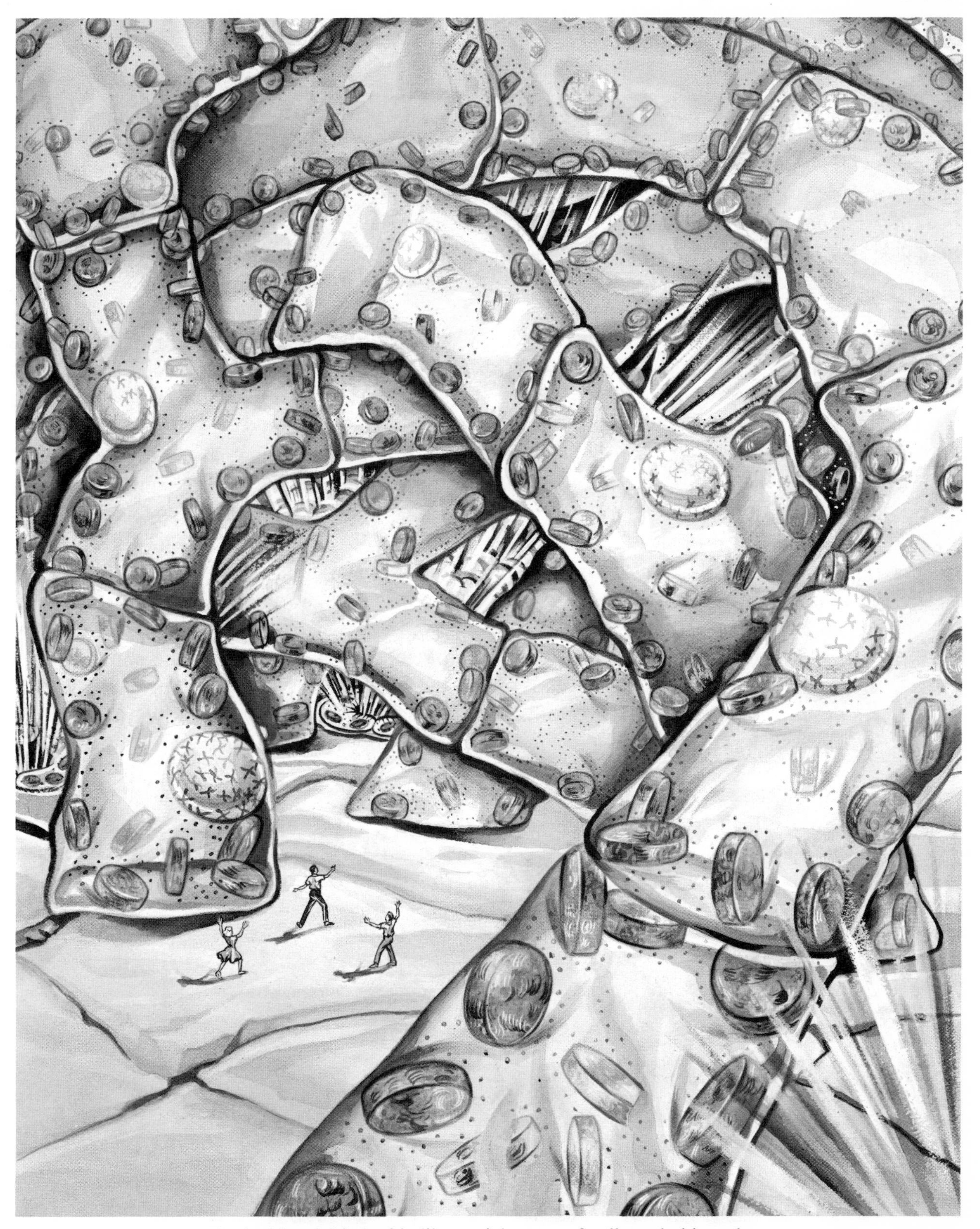

The inside of this leaf is like a nightmare of cells and chloroplasts.

Food-Making By Green Plants

CLOSE your eyes and imagine a tremendous stick of candy. See if you can imagine a stick of candy that stretches from your front yard to the sun! Also imagine that this stick of candy is three feet in diameter! Did you have trouble thinking of a stick of candy 93,000,000 (93 million) miles long and 3 feet wide? Yet, such a stick of candy is made every year by plants! Of course, the sugar is not in the form of a candy stick; a little of the candy sugar is made inside each living green plant.

How do plants make all this sugar? What does the sugar factory inside the plant look like? Well, that is what we want to explore on our adventure today!

We will have to crawl inside the green leaves of plants to visit the food-making factory. You made that trip before when we visited the cell, so you already know the way. Here, take a reducing pill and find your way into a leaf! I will follow you, this time. Ready? O.K., here we go! Next stop, a green cell inside. .a. . .l. .e. .a. . .f. . .f. . .f. . .

See how everything looks so green? Sunlight is shining through the green chloroplasts of all these leaf cells. Let's crawl into this cell and catch a ride on a chloroplast! As we ride around the cell, we can peer inside the chloroplast and watch sugar being made. Here comes a chloroplast now. Quick! Hop on!

Remember when we visited a cell on our last adventure, I said that food is made inside each chloroplast? Put your face close to this chloroplast and look inside. You should be able to see photosynthesis taking place. Oh, did I forget to explain what photosynthesis is? Look at the word and you will see what it means. "Photo" means light, just as in "photograph," which is a picture taken in light. "Synthesis" means to put things together; to make things. Now put the two words together: *photosynthesis,* to make things in light. The thing that is made is sugar, the same kind of sugar that you like to eat in candy. The sugar is food to a plant. Plants make their own food by photosynthesis. Now can you see why

Look inside this chloroplast. You can see food being made.

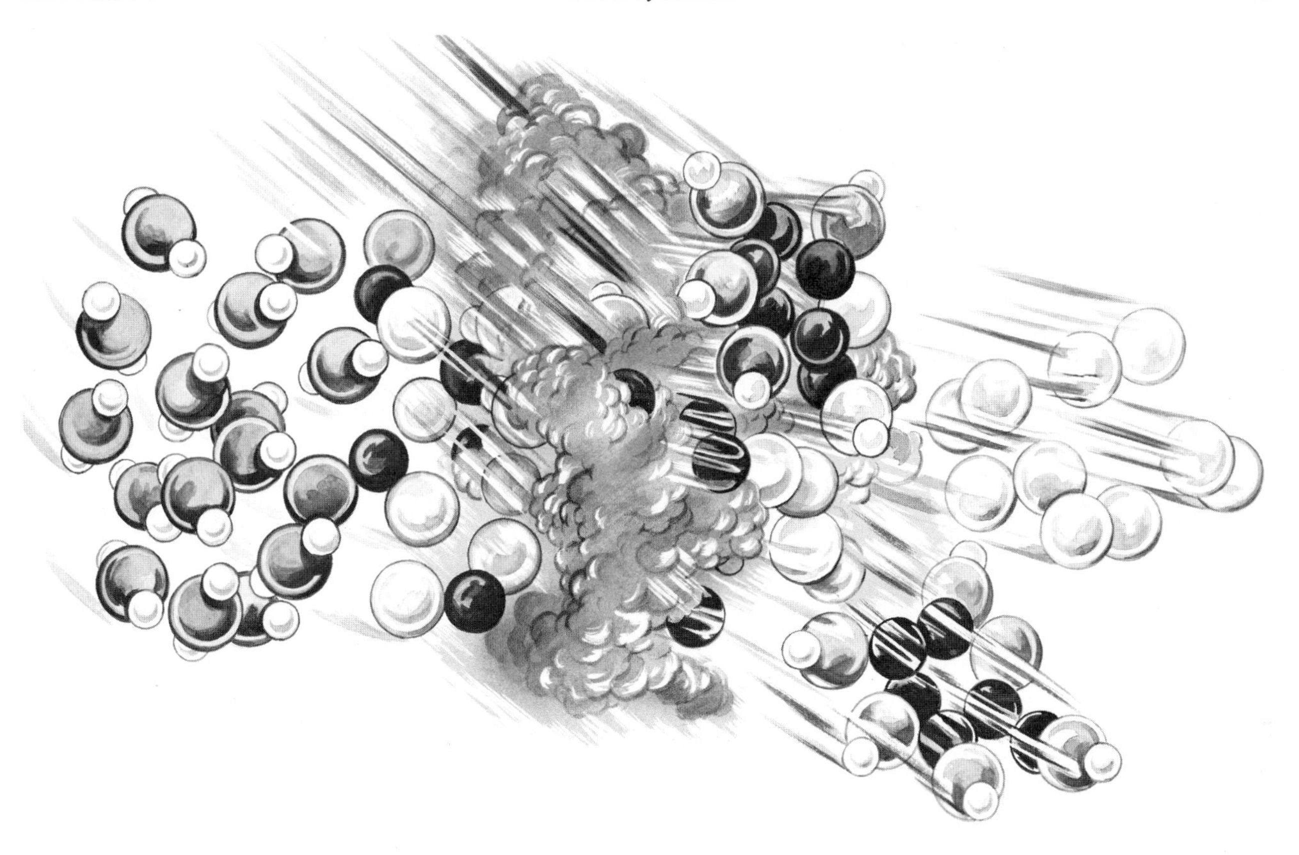

See those molecules of carbon dioxide and water going behind the molecules of chlorophyll? Sugar and oxygen molecules will come out from behind the chlorophyll.

plants need light to grow? Right; they need the light so they can make food (sugar).

See those small, flat green disks lined up side by side like a pile of pennies? Each of those disks has molecules of chlorophyll in it. The chlorophyll molecules catch rays of sunlight. See the sunlight shining on those molecules of chlorophyll? And can you see some of the chlorophyll wiggling back and forth? Those chlorophyll molecules that are wiggling have caught some sunlight energy and it makes them move. Look! See those flea-like objects around the wiggling chlorophyll molecules? They are water molecules. Each water molecule is made of two hydrogen atoms and one oxygen atom. That's why water is called H_2O. Now, if you watch closely, you'll see each water molecule get broken into its three atoms. There; some molecules of water just got broken apart! See the oxygen atoms from the water molecules forming gas bubbles? And there go the hydrogen atoms from the water. Whoops! They disappeared behind those chlorophyll molecules. See those other small molecules also going behind the chlorophyll? They are molecules of carbon dioxide. No one knows exactly what goes on back there, but watch for a moment. You'll see a sugar molecule come out from behind the chlorophyll. Here it comes now!

What happens back there? Well, we know that the hydrogens from water combine with the carbon dioxide, and form sugar. Some brilliant scientists are trying to find out what else happens behind those chlorophyll molecules. A chemist, Dr. Melvin Calvin, and a botanist, Dr. Daniel Arnon, have learned the most about the secrets of photosynthesis. They would agree, though, that much is still to be found.

Let me tell you again, step-by-step, what is happening while you watch it happen. First,

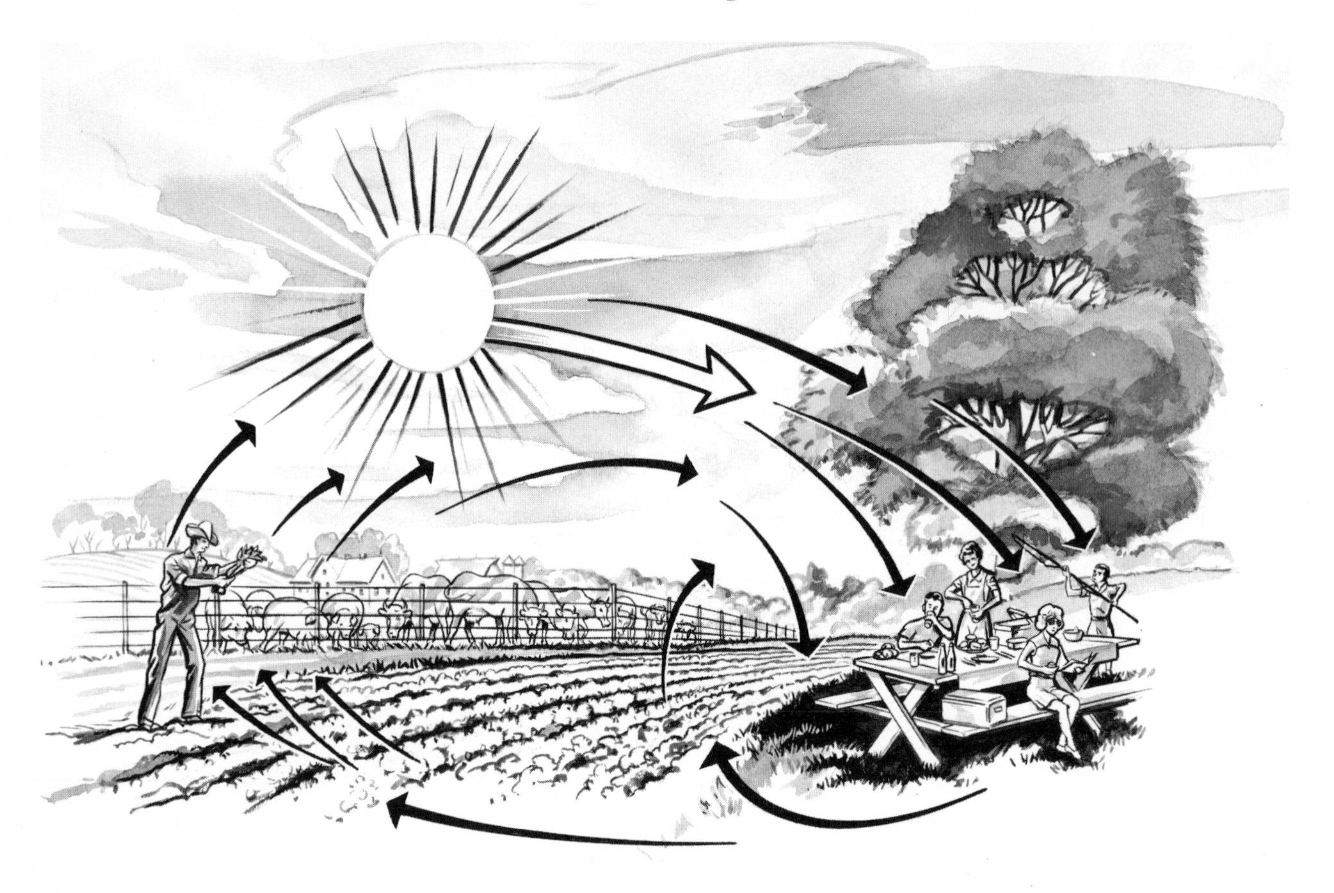

Plants use light, water, and carbon dioxide to make food and oxygen. Both plants and animals use the food and oxygen to keep alive.

chlorophyll catches some energy in sunlight. The energy makes chlorophyll excited and it wiggles. Then the chlorophyll uses the light energy to break apart water. The water breaks into one atom of oxygen and two atoms of hydrogen. Finally the hydrogens combine with carbon dioxide to form sugar. The oxygen atoms go together and form oxygen gas.

Usually when photosynthesis is going on very fast in a leaf, the sugar molecules are changed into starch. You probably already know what starch is; starch is a food found in many plants. A lot of starch is in potatoes, apples, corn, and beans. See those long spring-shaped molecules inside the chloroplast? They are starch molecules that were made from sugar. That is the way the plant stores the sugar for future use.

I wish I could show you more of what goes on inside chloroplasts. Perhaps you will become a scientist and will make some discoveries about how plants make food! Then we will be able to look inside the chloroplast and see more than we can now!

As we watch photosynthesis some more, let's think about why food-making by plants is important to you and me. What would we eat if plants did not make food? We wouldn't have lettuce, corn, potatoes, or any vegetables or fruits. And we wouldn't have meat to eat either! Cows, pigs and other animals get their food from plants. Let's not forget that when plants make food, they also make oxygen. You and I need oxygen to breathe. If it weren't for plants making oxygen, you and I and other animals would use up all the oxygen in the air and die!

Oh, oh! I can feel myself starting to get large again! I've got to leave! See you on the next ad. . .vent. . . . .ure. . . . . .

Things to Do and Think About

1. A look at the sides of leaves. Through a microscope or with a good magnifying glass, look at the underside of some leaves. Does the surface of the leaf look smooth? Can you see any hairs? Can you find the stomates? Are the stomates too small to see with a magnifying glass? Do these observations again, but this time look at the top surface of each leaf. Are the top and bottom surfaces of a leaf alike?

2. Is the green color of chlorophyll the only color in leaves? Let's see! Be careful *not* to do this experiment near flames.

Things you will need are: bottle of rubbing alcohol (may be bought at the drugstore); 3 drinking glasses of the same size and with smooth rims; toothpick; fresh, green leaves of grass, spinach, beets, or other leaves; a few sheets of white paper towels, white art paper, or other soft, white paper (do not use hard writing paper); scissors; knife.

Cut the fresh, green leaves into many tiny pieces with the scissors. Put the pieces in a glass and add 1 or 2 teaspoons of rubbing alcohol. With the point of the scissors, mash and stir the leaves in the alcohol. Do this for 3 or 4 minutes; the alcohol should get very green. The chlorophyll and other colored pigments in the leaves are being dissolved in the alcohol. Now take one sheet of the soft, white paper and carefully make 3 straight cuts in it as shown by the dotted lines in the drawing. Be careful not to get the paper dirty; be sure your hands and the knife are clean.

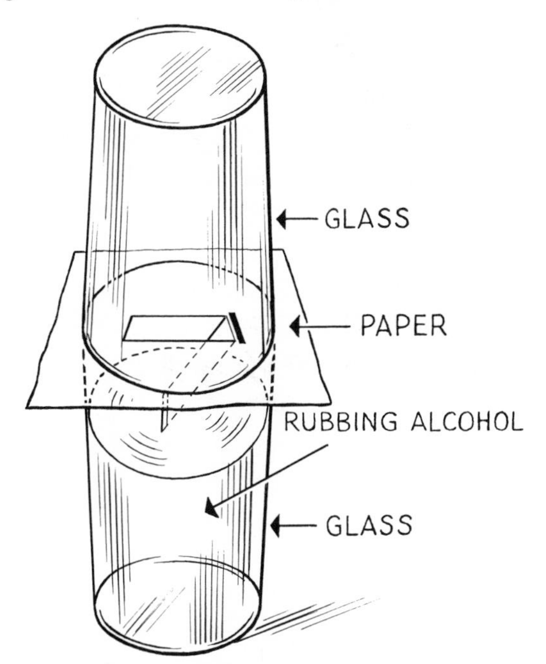

Next, dip the toothpick in the green-alcohol solution. Remove the toothpick and quickly draw the wet end of it across the paper; see the drawing for the exact place to do this on the paper. Blow on the paper to help make the alcohol evaporate. Dip the toothpick a second time in the green-alcohol solution. Quickly draw it across the same part of the paper. When the green stripe on the paper is nearly dry, do this a third time. Keep doing this until the little green stripe on the paper is a dark green. You may have to draw the wet toothpick across the paper 20 or 30 times before the stripe gets a dark color.

Now you are ready to chromatograph the plant pigments. Fold the paper so the little strip of paper in the middle bends down. Pour rubbing alcohol into a clean glass until the level of alcohol is 1/2 inch from the rim of the glass. Carefully set the paper on the rim of the glass of alcohol so that the little strip of paper bends down and dips into the alcohol. Be very careful not to get alcohol on the dark green stripe when you do this. Quickly take the third clean glass and turn it upside down on top of the paper and glass of alcohol. Once the set-up is all together do not move it until the chromatograph is finished. This will take about 15 minutes.

If everything has been done right, the alcohol will move up the paper strip. The paper is like a blotter. Then the alcohol gets to the colored stripe you made on the paper. The pigments dissolve in the alcohol. As the alcohol moves farther on the paper, the colored pigments move on the paper too. But some of the colors move faster than other colors. After the alcohol has moved an inch past the green stripe, each colored pigment should be in a separate place on the paper. This separation of things on a paper strip is called *paper chromatography*. The colored paper strip is called the *chromatogram*.

Do not be discouraged if your first chromatogram doesn't work very well. Try it several times. You will find that with patience and practice, your chromatograms will get better and better. The alcohol in the bottom glass can be used over and over again; so keep trying!

After you have learned how to make good chromatograms, try making chromatograms of different kinds of plants. A chromatogram of a carrot root will have a nice orange spot of *carotene*. A chromatogram of corn seeds will give a yellow spot of *xanthophyll*. Chromatograms of green plants have two main colors: orange-yellow color of carotene and xanthophyll, and the green color of chlorophyll.

Try making chromatograms of other things too:
- different kinds of ink (spot the ink directly on the paper strips)
- dry flower petals
- dry butterfly wings
- dry tomato fruit
- dry cantaloupe fruit
- food coloring (spot directly on the paper strips)
- sea weeds (if you live along the coast)
- dried green scum from ponds, irrigation ditches, etc.

Does each color and kind of pigment always move to the same place on different chromatograms? Do different plants contain the same amount of each colored pigment?

3. Let's see if plants do photosynthesis. Get a quart of green scum from a pond or use several sprigs of water plants from an aquarium. Put the plants in a soda pop bottle. Fill the bottle to the very top with pond water or fresh water. Add one fourth of a teaspoon of baking soda (sodium bicarbonate) to the water in the pop bottle. Next turn a pan (pie plate or pot) upside down and lay it on top of the bottle. Hold both firmly so that the mouth of the pop bottle is flat against the pan. Now turn the pan and bottle together so the pan is rightside up and the bottle is upside down. Do not let air bubbles get into the bottle. If they do, start over again. Now add some water to the inside of the pan until it is about one-half inch deep.

Put the set-up in a place where it will get bright light most of the day. Keep the set-up where the water in the jar does not get hot or chilled. Do bubbles of gas start coming from the plants after a few minutes or hours? What kind of gas is it?

Leave the set-up until one fourth or one-half the bottle is filled with gas. This may take several hours or a day or two. Now, over a sink, turn the set-up the way it was at the start of the experiment. Do not let any air get into the jar when you do this. Next wet one of your hands. Slide your hand in between the top of the bottle and the pan. Try to keep the gas inside the jar from getting out; keep air from going into the jar. Keep your hand tightly over the jar.

Now have someone light a wood match. Let the match burn for a few seconds. Then quickly do this: blow out the match flame; quickly slide your hand away from the jar; stick the hot glowing match into the gas in the jar. What happens? Does the glowing match burst into flame? What kind of gas was collected in the jar?

Would bubbles of gas collect in the jar if the set-up were in a dark closet instead of in the light? Try it!

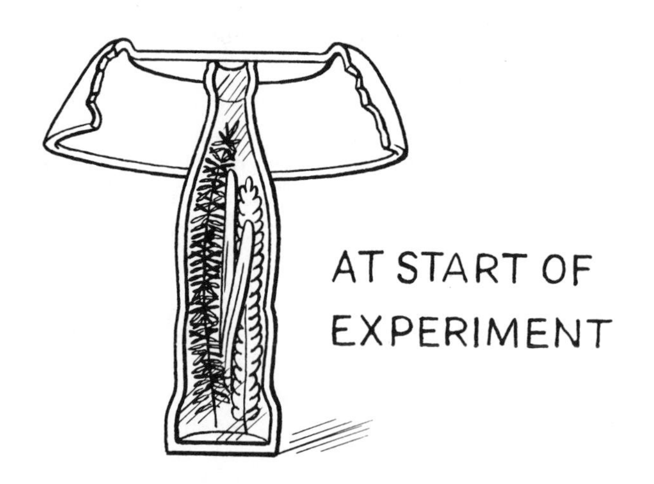

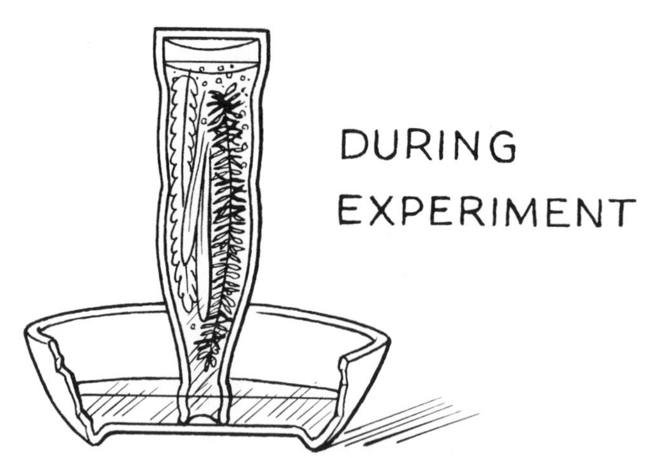

ADVENTURE 4
Burning Food In Cells
RESPIRATION

Enzymes are the machinery of respiration. They cut food molecules into smaller pieces, and energy is released.

Burning Food In Cells

I HOPE the name of this adventure doesn't scare you! This twenty-five cent word, respiration, simply stands for the way you and plants and animals burn food to release energy. You are respiring right now. If you weren't you wouldn't be here! All living cells respire. About half the energy that you release when you respire is heat energy. Heat energy warms you. The other half of the energy released in your cells as you respire can be used by you to do things. When you run and play, or work hard, you respire and burn food rapidly inside your body. As the food is burned, it is broken apart and energy is released. Your muscles use this energy to make your legs move, your eyes move and focus, or whatever you are doing. Even when you are asleep your cells respire. After all, it takes energy to make your heart beat, your lungs open and close, and your cells live and grow.

You know plants don't have muscles, hearts, or lungs, but they *are* made of cells that live and grow. And cells in plants also respire. In fact, plants respire almost the same way your cells respire. We can even say all cells respire about the same way—frogs, grasshoppers, trees, people, seaweed, monkeys, elephants—all respire in nearly the same way.

Imagine that you are standing inside an elephant cell watching it respire! I will stand inside a cell of a tree watching it respire. Will we both see about the same kind of respiration? We certainly will! Of course the elephant cell you are standing in looks reddish because of the elephant blood. And the cell of the tree I am standing in looks greenish because of the chlorophyll. But as we watch these two cells respire, we both see about the same thing. I said "about" the same thing because these two cells do things just a little differently. If they didn't, an elephant would look like a tree; or would the tree look like an elephant?

We said that in respiration food is burned and energy is released for use by the body. Is the food burned in your body the same way food is burned in a fire? Will the amount of energy released in your body cells and in the fire be the same? Suppose you respire a candy bar; also suppose a similar candy bar is burned in a fire. The candy bar will burn differently in your cells than in the fire; but the *amount* of energy released will be the same! In the fire, the energy is released as heat and light. Inside your body, half the energy is released as heat; the other half can be used by your body. But the *total amount* of energy released when food is burned in your body or in the fire is the same!

We can burn food in a fire and find out how much energy is in the food. That is the way doctors, chemists, dieticians, and others find how much heat energy is in things. These people find the number of *calories* of heat energy released when food is burned.

Do you know what a calorie is? One calorie is the amount of heat needed to raise the temperature of one milliliter of water one degree Celsius (1.8° Fahrenheit).

Just so we don't get confused, people who want to lose weight talk about *Calories* which are really *kilocalories. Kilo* means one thousand, so you can see that there are 1000 calories in one kilocalorie. It takes this 1000 calories (one kilocalorie) to raise the

Both plants and animals respire—that is burn food and release energy—but they do it in different ways.

temperature of one liter of water 1.0° Celsius (1.8° Fahrenheit). Kilocalories, then, are larger than the calories we talk about in this book.

You would probably like to know how many calories of heat energy are in some of the foods you eat, like table sugar. If you burn 342 grams (about 3/4 of a pound) of sugar, 1,349,000 calories are released! That is a lot of calories! It is enough calories to make two quarts of ice at the freezing point (0° C. or 32° F.) turn into steam at 100° C. (212° F.)! Now, what happens when you eat a candy bar or a large serving of potatoes? Will the many thousands of calories released when your body respires this food make your blood boil? Will you start to steam and sizzle? It seems you should get "cooked" from the inside! You know already that the answer to all of these questions must be: NO! But do you know why? When sugar is burned in a fire, all the heat energy is released at one time. That is what makes the fire so hot. But when you respire sugar in your body, energy is released slowly—a little at a time. Your body uses half the energy as it is released. The other half of the energy released is heat energy. The heat is released slowly, too; your body gets rid of it and keeps cool—you don't sizzle!

Now for the hard question: How does respiration work in a cell? How is it done? This problem has puzzled many brilliant men for hundreds of years; not many answers were found until recently. Biochemists are still exploring the inside of cells trying to find out how cells work. Let's see some of the things they have found.

Every living cell is respiring; enzymes are the machinery of this respiration. Remember when we explored the inside of a cell? We saw thousands of different enzymes floating in the cytoplasm. Some enzymes we saw were respiratory enzymes. Each of these enzymes has a special job in respiration. One enzyme breaks starch into sugars. Another enzyme cuts each sugar molecule in half. Other enzymes cut these pieces of sugar into smaller pieces. Finally all that is left of the sugar are molecules of carbon dioxide (CO_2). Animal cells don't have much use for carbon dioxide so they get rid of it. In your body, the carbon dioxide collects in your lungs and you breathe it out. In plants, the carbon dioxide is lost to the air around the cell as well as around the entire plant.

I forgot to mention one very important thing! Can you think of it? Maybe this hint will help you. Why does a fire go out when it is smothered? That's right; a fire needs air to burn. Do you know what is in air that helps a fire burn? It is oxygen gas. Now do you know what I forgot to say about burning sugar in your body? Did you guess it? Your cells need oxygen to respire sugar. That is why you have to breathe air faster. Do you see why? You respire faster when you run, and that means more oxygen is needed! Cells of plants need oxygen for respiration, too. When oxygen is used in respiration more energy is released from the food for the plant or animal to use.

To make this story complete, I must tell you that some organisms don't need oxygen for their respiration. Some bacteria, yeasts and other fungi can live without oxygen. Can you guess if they are able to get much energy out of sugar when they burn it in their bodies? You're right; they get very little energy! Let's look at a yeast cell. A yeast cell uses sugar for its food. It respires the sugar and forms alcohol and carbon dioxide. If we touch a lighted match to some alcohol, the alcohol burns with a very hot flame. This shows that alcohol has a lot of heat energy in it. It also tells us that a yeast cell gets very little energy out of the sugar it respires. Most of the energy stays in the alcohol; the yeast cell can't obtain the energy from the alcohol.

We have seen that there are two kinds of respiration. Most animals and plants use oxygen for their respiration. This kind of respiration is called *aerobic respiration.* The word "aerobic" means "with air (oxygen)." Some organisms do not use oxygen in respiration. This kind of respiration is *anaerobic.* The "*an*" of "*anaerobic*" means "*without,*" so *anaerobic respiration* means "respiration without air."

What happens to the energy released when food is respired? Some goes off as heat and can't be used except to warm the body. The rest of the energy is used to help *make* things or *do* things. You use energy to help *make* things like fats, muscles, chromosomes, brain cells, and all the other things inside you. You also use energy to *do* things, such as moving your arms and legs, thinking and growing. Plants also use energy to help *make* things and to help *do* things. Plants use energy to help make cell walls, fats, chloroplasts, enzymes, and everything else that is inside plant cells. Plants also use energy to grow, to take minerals from the soil, and to move

Without oxygen, less energy is released in respiration.

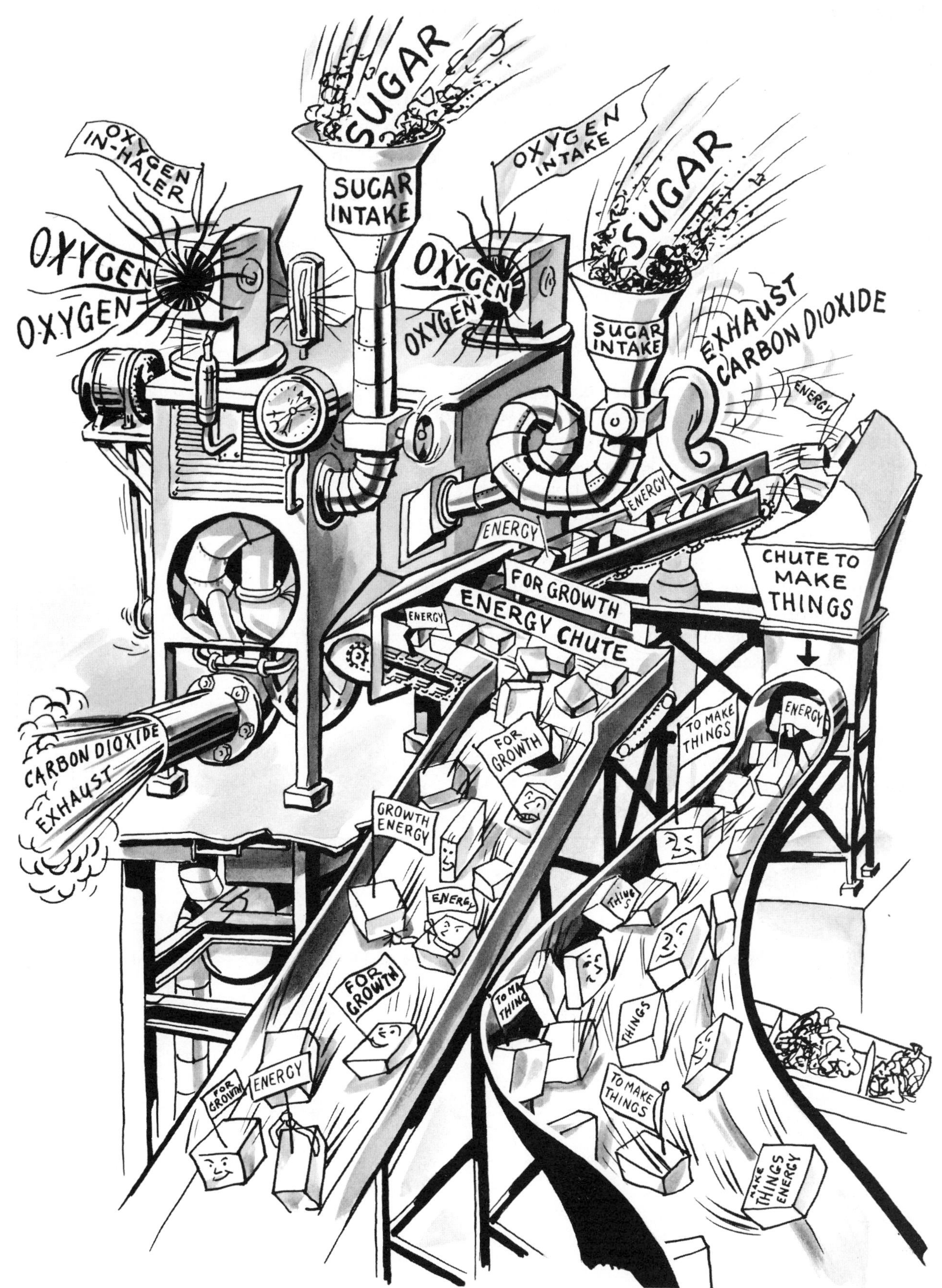

In go food and oxygen; out come energy and exhaust. This machine is like respiration.

things from one place to another. We will explore other ways that plants use energy in later adventures.

I hope now you see that respiration in cells releases the energy that is in food—respiration releases power to do and make things. Your body is something like a car engine. A car burns gasoline and releases power to move the wheels of the car. Respiration in a cell burns food and also releases power. Gasoline is burned in the motor of your car in small explosions and the motor gets very hot. In this way energy is wasted. In the cells of plants and animals, food is burned slowly and the cells do not get hot. Over half the energy released in this way can be used to do and make things. The car engine and your body are alike in another way; the engine uses oxygen to burn the gasoline, and your body uses oxygen in respiration to burn food.

Things to Do and Think About

1. Can the heat released in respiration be measured? Get two small thermos bottles that are the same size, or close to the same size. If you don't have any thermos bottles, you can make them. To do this, use two clean, narrow olive jars. Wrap the outside and bottom of each jar with three or four layers of aluminum foil. Then wrap each bottle with about 6 layers of newspaper. Then wrap each bottle with a layer of aluminum foil. Use some tape to keep the layers wrapped tightly around the bottles.

Now, get a couple handfuls of dry seeds. Oats, corn, bean, or grass seeds of any kind work very well. Soak *half* the seeds in a glass of water for an hour. After an hour, pour off the extra water and put the soaked seeds in one of the thermos bottles. Put the dry seeds in the other thermos bottle. Label the bottle with the dry seeds "*bottle #1.*" Label the bottle with the soaked seeds "*bottle #2.*"

Next get some cotton and tightly plug the opening of each bottle. The experiment should now look like this:

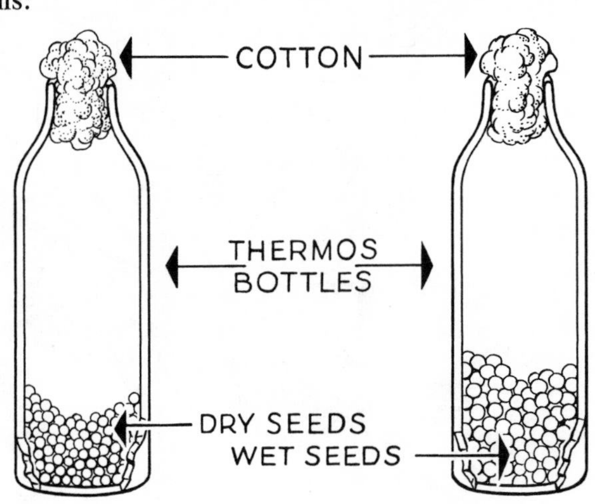

Time of Day	Date	Temperature (°C or °F) Bottle #1	Bottle #2	Time of Day	Date	Temperature (°C or °F) Bottle #1	Bottle #2
1.				8.			
2.				9.			
3.				10.			
4.				11.			
5.				12.			
6.				13.			
7.				14.			

Put a long thermometer through the cotton plug of bottle #1. Carefully push the thermometer into the bottle until the bulb of the thermometer is covered by the dry seeds. Wait 1 or 2 minutes and record the temperature. Remove the thermometer from bottle #1; get the temperature of bottle #2 in the same way. Record the time of day and the date. Put the temperatures, time, and date in the table on page 28.

Find the temperature of each bottle every day for the next 10 or 14 days. Always record the time of day when you get the temperatures. If you can, get the temperatures at the same time every day. Check your thermometer to see if it reads in degrees Centigrade or degrees Fahrenheit. Either will do, but be sure you know which kind of thermometer you are using.

After you have found the temperatures of the wet and dry seeds for 10 to 14 days, look at the seeds in each bottle. Also smell each bottle. What causes the odor? Would whatever made this odor affect the temperature in that bottle?

When the experiment is over, or during the experiment, use your results to make a graph of the temperatures. Plot your results in the graph on page 114. Use a blue pencil to connect the points on the graph for bottle #1; label the line "*dry seeds—bottle #1.*" Use a red pencil to connect the points on the graph for bottle #2; label this line "*wet seeds—bottle #2.*"

Can you explain the difference in temperature of the two bottles? What are the reasons for having bottle #1 in this experiment? What happened in bottle #2 that didn't happen in bottle #1? Where did the heat come from in each bottle? Try to account for the shape of the two lines on the graph. Why did the temperature in bottle #2 rise when it did?

2. How to find the amount of heat (calories) in food. Get permission from your parents or teacher before you do this experiment. It is best to do this experiment in a sink or on a sidewalk away from things that can catch fire.

Find a 2-pound coffee can or any can that is 8 to 10 inches tall and 5 or 6 inches wide. Be sure the can is not rusty. Now find a small can; a frozen orange juice can is just the right size. With a nail, trace the round end of the small can on the bottom of the large can. With a metal cutting scissors, hammer, and screwdriver, cut a hole in the bottom of the large can along the line you just traced. Be careful not to cut yourself in doing these things.

Now cut flaps in the upper rim of the small can so it looks like the drawing:

Next, about 2 inches from the rim on the side of the large can, draw a circle around the can. With a nail and hammer, punch 4 holes into the large can along the circle you have drawn. The holes should be 1/4 the distance around the can from each other. Now take some wire and put it through the holes in the can so it forms a "cross" inside the can. Follow the arrows in the diagram.

Now cut a door in the rim and side of the large can. Bend the three flaps on the small can outward. Put the small can through the hole in the large can. The flaps of the small can should rest on the bottom of the large can.

Now get a piece of wire screen one or two inches square. Lay it on top of the wire "cross" inside the large can. Lay a soda cracker on top of the screen inside the large can.

You have just made a *calorimeter!* This is an instrument to measure the amount of heat in a food. The heat will come from the cracker. Your calorimeter should look like the drawing below:

Accurately measure two fluid ounces of water; use a kitchen measuring cup. If you have a metric

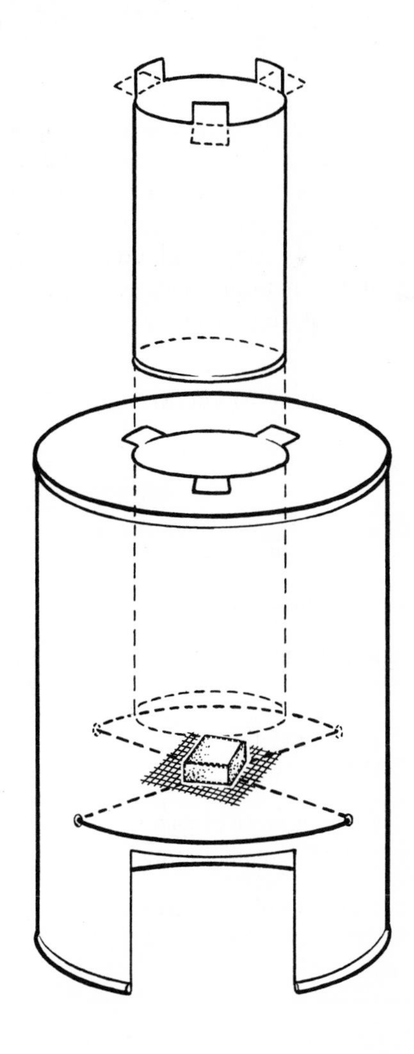

measuring cylinder, measure 59 milliliters of water. Pour the two ounces (59 milliliters) of water into the small can.

With a thermometer (in °F or °C) find the temperature of the water in the small can. Record this temperature in the table at the end of this experiment.

Place the calorimeter in a sink or on a sidewalk away from things that can catch fire. Be sure there is no breeze if you do this part of the experiment outside. Light a match and ignite the soda cracker in your calorimeter. As soon as the cracker starts burning, remove the match. Let the cracker burn completely. The cracker may stop burning before it is all burned up. If this happens, quickly re-ignite it with another match.

After the cracker has burned as much as it will, find the temperature of the water. Write it in the table.

Now find the weight of soda cracker. This can be done by weighing a soda cracker on an accurate balance; or by reading the label on the cracker box and finding the total weight of crackers in the box. Then find the number of crackers in this box when it is full; divide the total weight of crackers in the box by the number of crackers. Now fill in the table and do the figuring.

Try this experiment again using fresh water and another soda cracker. Do the results of the second test agree with the results from the first test? Can you account for any differences? Also try this experiment using other kinds of food, wood, etc. Be sure they are dry when you put them in the calorimeter. Burn only a small piece of material each time.

DATA FROM CALORIMETER STUDY

1. Substance tested	soda cracker
2. Volume of water in the calorimeter (2 ounces = 59 milliliters)	59 milliliters
3. Weight of substance tested	________
4. Temperature of water at END of experiment	________°
5. Temperature of water at BEGINNING of experiment	________°
6. Increase of temperature of water during experiment (item 4 minus item 5)	________
7. Number of calories of heat released when the substance burned (see "Hint" below)	________calories

3. Do germinating seeds respire? Do they use oxygen?
Things you will need for this experiment:

large test tube or long, narrow (1½") olive jar
handful of small seeds (oats, rye, corn, peas, etc.)
wad of cotton
pie pan, cereal bowl, or any container with a flat bottom

Soak the seeds in water for 1 to 2 hours. Then pour off the extra water. Pour the soaked seeds into a test tube or olive jar. Push a wad of cotton into the tube or jar; push the cotton against the seeds. The seeds should be held tightly enough so the container can be turned upside down without the seeds falling out. Stand the tube of seeds upside down in a flat-bottomed bowl. Pour water into the bowl until it is about 1 inch deep.

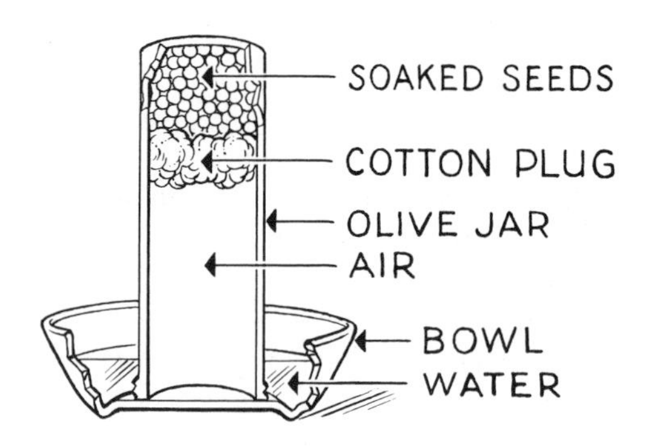

Put the set-up in a warm place, but not in sunlight or on a radiator.

Look at the set-up each day. Each day stand a ruler next to the jar and find how high the water is inside the jar. Record the height of water in the table below. Also record what the seeds look like each day (for example: Are they sprouting? Are they growing fast?). You may have to add water to the bowl during the experiment.

After 10 to 14 days, carry the set-up to a sink and carefully do this: put one hand under the bowl and hold the jar with your other hand; push them tightly together and then turn the set-up upside down. Now the bowl is a lid on top of the jar. Do this so that no air gets into the jar, and no gas gets out of the jar. Now light a match, remove the bowl slowly from the top of the jar, and quickly hold the match in the gas inside the jar. Does the match burn or go out? Why?

HINT: One calorie is the amount of heat that raises the temperature of 1 milliliter of water 1° Celsius (or 1.8° Fahrenheit).

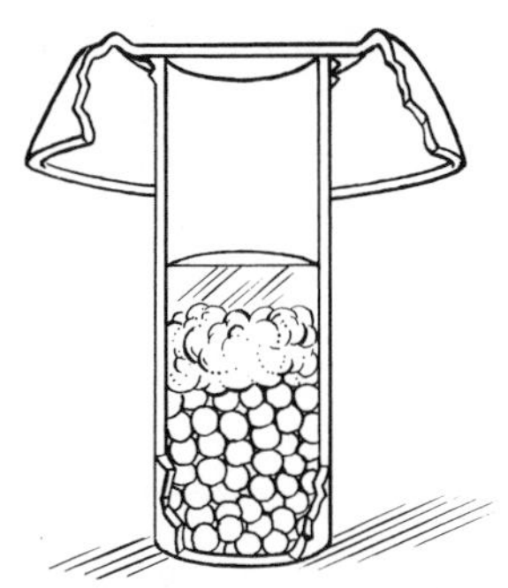

Why did the water rise in the jar? How do you know what gas was used up inside the jar? Did the water rise the same amount each day? Is the height the water rose related to how fast the seeds were growing? Did the water stop rising toward the end of the experiment? Did the seeds release any gas during the experiment? How could you test for this gas? Where did this gas go? Try drawing a graph of your results. In your graph put *"height of water in the jar"* on the vertical axis of the graph. Put *"date of measurement"* on the horizontal axis. Use the graph paper at the end of this book.

	Date and time of day	Appearance of seeds	Height of water in jar
1.			
2.			
3.			
4.			
5.			
6.			
7.			
8.			
9.			
10.			
11.			
12.			
13.			
14.			

Try doing this experiment again, but this time keep the set-up in a refrigerator for 10 to 14 days. Compare the results of the two experiments – the first in a warm place, the second in a cool place. Can you explain why the results are so different? Can you now explain these things? See if you can!

Cold-blooded animals move very slowly on cold days.
Grass lawns have to be mowed more often in the summer than in the spring and fall.
Trees grow very little in the winter.
Food and milk kept in a refrigerator spoil slowly; food and milk kept in a warm room spoil rapidly.

4. An exciting experiment with an enzyme. This is an experiment that goes fast and is lots of fun. You will need to buy two things for it:

one large potato
½ pint bottle of 10% or 20% hydrogen peroxide at a drugstore (sometimes called 10 volumes or 20 volumes of hydrogen peroxide)

You will also need a knife, a *glass* bowl or *glass* baking dish, a long narrow drinking glass or olive jar, and some wood matches.

If you bought 10 per cent hydrogen peroxide, carefully pour it all into the glass bowl; then fill the bottle twice with water and add the water each time to the peroxide in the bowl. If you bought 20 per cent hydrogen peroxide, pour all of it into the glass bowl; then fill the bottle 6 times with water and pour the 6 bottles of water into the peroxide in the bowl. Now the hydrogen peroxide is about 3 per cent no matter what strength of peroxide you bought.

Next, cut the potato into slices about ⅛ inch thick. Put 10 to 20 slices in the long, narrow drinking glass or olive jar. Fill the glass or jar with 3% hydrogen peroxide. Put your hand tightly over the glass jar; quickly turn the container upside down. Now lower it into the bowl of 3 per cent hydrogen peroxide; remove your hand, and let the jar stand in the bowl. The set-up should look like this:

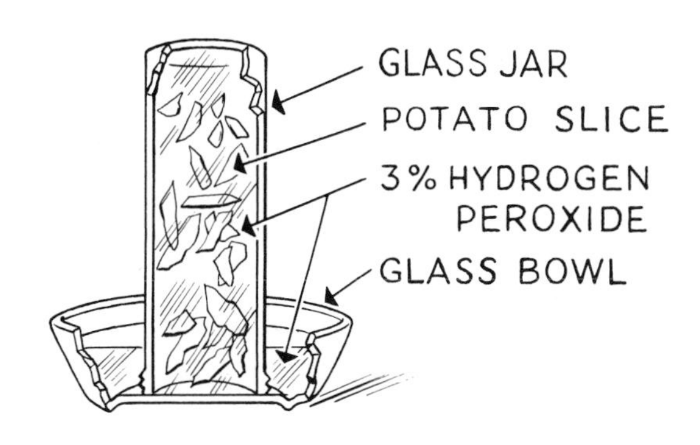

What do you see happening inside the inverted jar? Where do the bubbles come from?

After the jar or glass has filled with gas, slip your hand under the opening of the container. With your hand tightly against the opening, lift the jar of gas from the bowl and then turn it right-side-up. Be sure to keep your hand tightly over the opening. Have someone light a wood match. When the match is burning well, blow out the flame; remove your hand from the jar and quickly hold the still red-hot match in the gas in the jar. What happens? What kind of gas is in the jar?

You can do this experiment many times with the same 3 per cent hydrogen peroxide and potato slices.

Here is the chemical reaction of what is going on:

$$2H_2O_2 \xrightarrow{\text{catalase}} 2H_2O + O_2$$

Catalase is the name of an enzyme; it is made inside potato cells. Catalase takes 2 molecules of hydrogen peroxide and changes them into 2 molecules of water and 1 molecule of oxygen. And one molecule of catalase does this millions of times each minute!

Most animal and plant cells have molecules of catalase in them. Hydrogen peroxide is a by-product of respiration in most cells; the catalase helps to get rid of it.

Have you ever put hydrogen peroxide on a cut or scab on your body? Did it fizz? Why did the cut or scab fizz when hydrogen peroxide was put on it? Do your cells contain catalase?

Try some other kinds of plants (apple slices, lettuce leaves, celery, cabbage, radish, etc.) Find out if their cells have catalase in them.

5. Yeast cells do anaerobic respiration. Buy a package of powdered yeast or yeast cake at the grocery store. Next take a tablespoon of Karo syrup or sugar and mix it with a quart of warm water. Pour the package of yeast in a tall olive jar; add a little of the sugar-water and stir the yeast into it. The yeast-sugar-water mixture should be like a thick paste. Now fill the jar with the rest of the sugar-water mixture. Turn a pie pan or bowl upside down on top of the jar. Carefully turn the pan and jar upside down; don't let any of the mixture leak out of the jar. The set-up should look like this:

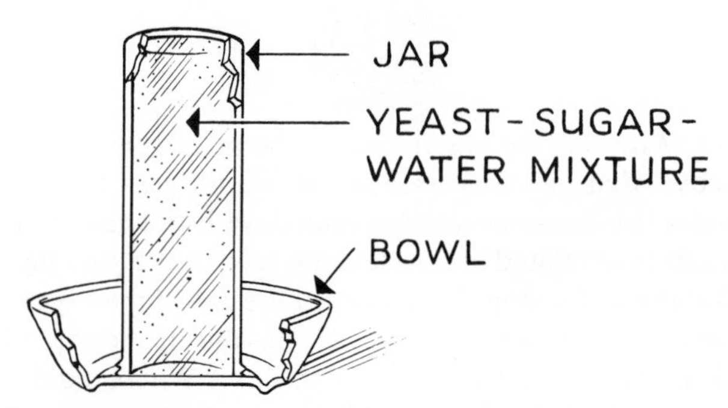

Put the set-up in a warm place. Record the time. Find how long it takes for the jar to half-fill with gas. When the jar is half-filled with gas, test the gas with a burning match (experiment #3 tells how to do this). What happens to the match flame? Smell the yeast-sugar-water mixture. Do you recognize the odor?

Now pour all the yeast-sugar-water mixture back into the jar. Fix the set-up as before; do the experiment again, but this time put the set-up in a refrigerator. Find the time it takes for the jar to fill half-way with gas. Can you explain why it takes a different length of time in the refrigerator than in the warm room?

If your mother will let you, try the experiment again by putting the set-up in the oven of her stove. Set the stove for 200°F. or as close to that as the stove can go. How long does it take for the jar to half-fill with gas? Try to explain the results.

What will happen if you do these experiments again, but using only a yeast-water mixture and leaving out the sugar? Try it and see!

ADVENTURE 5

What Plants Take From Soil

NUTRITION

"What happened to the missing two ounces of soil?" In 1600, a Dutch scientist did an experiment to find out.

What Plants Take From Soil

Adventure 5
Nutrition

In our adventures in cells we saw plants make many things. We also found that plants need water (H_2O), carbon dioxide (CO_2) and oxygen (O_2) to do many things. Where do plants get these materials? We all know that plants get water from the soil. Carbon dioxide and oxygen gas come from the air in the soil and around the leaves and stems. Are these the only chemicals that plants need? Can plants make all the things that are found inside them if they have enough water, carbon dioxide, and oxygen?

A Dutchman named van Helmont asked himself this question in 1600. He couldn't find the answer in any books, so he decided to do an experiment. Van Helmont decided to grow a plant in a known amount of soil. Then, after the plant grew very large, he would weigh the soil again. If the soil lost weight he would know that the plant used some of the soil.

To start the experiment he got a large pot of dry soil. He weighed the soil very carefully and then planted a small willow tree in it. When he watered the plant he always used rainwater because it is pure water; no dirt or other things are mixed in it. Van Helmont also put a cover over the soil to keep dust from falling into the pot. He let the plant grow for five years until it was a large tree. Then van Helmont carefully pulled all the roots out of the pot of soil. He was very careful not to spill any of the soil. He then let the soil dry out; after it was dry he weighed the soil. To his surprise, the pot of soil didn't weigh as much as it did at the beginning of the experiment, five years before. Here are the weights of soil that van Helmont wrote in his notebook:

Weight of soil in pot at beginning
of experiment: 300 pounds
Weight of soil in pot at end of experiment
5 years later: 299 pounds and 14 ounces

Weight of soil lost from pot
during experiment: 2 ounces

Two ounces of soil weren't in the pot anymore. Where did the two ounces of soil go? Where do you think the soil went?

For many years scientists thought that plants get food from the soil. But now we know that plants make their own food by photosynthesis. Then *what* do plants get from the soil? The answer was found only in the past 50 years. Botanists found that plants get minerals from the soil. Some of the minerals are needed in large amounts, and others are needed in very small amounts. Here are the minerals that plants have to get from soil:

Needed by plants in large amounts
Phosphorus (phosphate minerals)
Potassium
Nitrogen (nitrate minerals)
Sulfur (sulfate minerals)
Calcium
Magnesium
Iron

Needed by plants in small amounts
Boron (borate minerals)
Copper
Chlorine (chloride minerals)
Molybdenum (molybdate minerals)
Zinc
Manganese
Cobalt

There may be other minerals needed by plants, too; if there are others, they are needed in extremely small amounts.

What happens to a plant if it doesn't get all these minerals? The answer is simple: the plant gets very sick! What would happen to your bones and teeth if you didn't drink lots of milk? You would have very weak bones and teeth and you would feel sick! Why? Because milk has calcium in it, and calcium is needed to build strong teeth and bones. A plant doesn't have teeth and bones, but it does need a special glue to hold its cells next to each other. Calcium is used to make this glue. If there isn't enough calcium to make the glue, then the plant looks very sick and usually dies. You can usually find sick plants in your neighborhood. Look for grass lawns that are yellow or a very light green color, or shrubs and trees that are yellowish or do not have large, healthy leaves.

Each of the minerals that a plant uses does special jobs in the plant. All the jobs each mineral does have not been found. Here are some of the findings, so far.

phosphorus	used in respiration and photosynthesis; part of chromosomes
potassium	no one knows what it is needed for!
nitrogen	part of chlorophyll, enzymes, chromosomes, and many other things in cells
sulfur	part of enzymes
calcium	used to make the glue that holds cells next to each other
magnesium	part of chlorophyll
iron	needed to make chlorophyll; also used in respiration.

Botanists and biochemists haven't found exactly what the minerals that are used in small amounts do inside plants. Maybe one of the boys or girls in your school will become a scientist and discover what these minerals do in plants. Maybe that boy or girl will be you!

While I think of it, your body needs the same minerals plants do. And the minerals do almost the same jobs in your cells as they do in plant cells! In fact, all plant and animal cells use minerals in nearly the same way. How do you get these minerals into your

Of course plants can get sick! Here only those marked "COMP" are healthy. Each of the others is sick because it did not receive one of the essential minerals: nitrogen (N), phosphorus (P), potassium (K), magnesium (Mg), sulfur (S), and calcium (Ca).

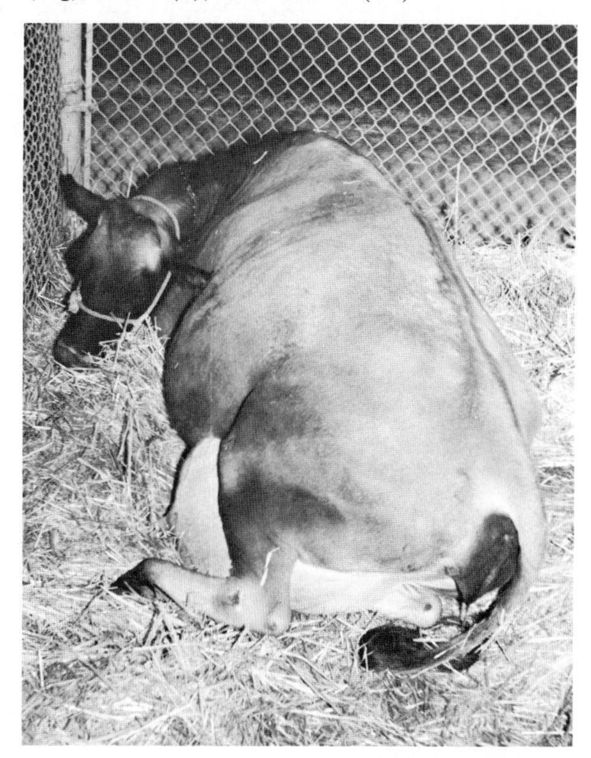

Not only plants and people, but animals can suffer from lack of essential minerals. This cow has *milk fever* because she isn't getting enough calcium. She is sleepy, bloated, and too weak even to stand up.

body? You don't eat a big serving of soil for dinner, that's for sure! Then how do you get the minerals you need? You simply eat some plants—lettuce, carrots, potatoes, spinach, peas, beans, corn—and all the other plant foods. You can also get these minerals by eating other animals or parts of animals—fish, hot dogs, steak, chicken. When these animals were alive they ate plants; so the minerals in the meat you eat came from plants. And the plants got the minerals from the soil.

You probably never thought about this before: how many ways do our lives depend upon plants? Let's not count uses of plants for clothing, building houses, or for keeping your house warm. Let's only think of ways that plants help you and me to stay alive. How many ways can you think of?

Things to Do and Think About

1. What are cells made of? If you haven't done Experiment 2 of Adventure 2, try it now. If you have done this experiment, find the results in your notebook and think about them again; you may be able to get some more ideas about the results now!

2. Some experiments with soils. Find 2 kinds of soil for this group of experiments. Find a very sandy soil; the sand from a child's sandpile will do fine. Get about a gallon of it. Also find a non-sandy soil that has very little sand in it. If you rub a non-sandy soil between your fingers, it should feel smooth. Get about a gallon of this non-sandy soil. Spread the soils in two piles on newspapers and let them dry out.

Do each of the following experiments with both soils. Write the results in the table at the end of the experiments. You should do this experiment where it won't matter if you make a mess!

Experiment "A"

A. Find empty vegetable cans that each have a volume of about one pint. The two cans should be the same size. Use a kitchen measuring cup and some water and find the total volume of each can.

Fill one can with the sandy soil; fill the other can with the non-sandy soil. Be careful not to pack the soil into the cans. The soil should fill each can level with the top. Now fill a kitchen measuring cup with water to the top mark. Pour the water slowly into one of the cans of soil. Keep adding water to the can until the soil stops bubbling and the can is filled to the top with water. Record the volume of water used to fill the can of soil with water. Do the same thing with the second can of soil. Save the two cans of wet soil for experiment "B."

	Sandy Soil	Non-Sandy Soil
1. Volume of empty can	________	________
2. Volume of water needed to fill the can of soil	________	________
3. Percent of air in the dry soil $\left(\frac{\text{item 2} \times 100}{\text{item 1}}\right)$	________%	________%
4. Volume of soil particles in the can (item 1 – item 2)	________	________

Experiment "B"

B. Take two quart or half-gallon paper milk cartons and cut off the spout end. Pour each of the wet soils from experiment "A" into the milk cartons. Rinse the metal cans with a little water and pour the rinse water into the proper milk carton. Now add enough water to each milk carton to bring the water level to within 2 inches of the top. Get 2 long spoons; stir each soil-water mixture rapidly. Be careful not to spill any of the mixtures.

Take one of the cartons of soil and water; stir it rapidly and then suddenly stop stirring. Use a watch with a second hand, and wait exactly 40 seconds after you stop stirring. Then quickly, but smoothly, pour the water out of the milk carton. DO NOT pour off the sand that has settled to the bottom of the milk carton. Now pour all the sand from the milk carton into a kitchen measuring cup. Measure the volume of sand.

The soil that doesn't settle in 40 seconds is in the water that was poured off. This part of the soil is made of *clay* and *silt* particles. They are much smaller than sand particles; they do not settle as rapidly as sand does because they are smaller. Subtract the volume of sand from the total volume of dry soil you started with; now you will know the volume of silt and clay in the soil.

Do the last part of this experiment over again with the second carton of water and soil. Record all results in the table.

6. Volume of soil used (item 1 from Expt. A)	________	________
7. Volume of sand that settled in 40 seconds	________	________
8. Percent volume of sand in soil $\left(\frac{\text{item 7 x 100}}{\text{item 6}}\right)$	________%	________%
9. Percent volume of clay and silt in soil $\left(\frac{\text{item 6} - \text{item 7}}{\text{item 6}} \text{ x 100}\right)$	________%	________%

Experiment "C"

C. Take the two empty cans from experiment "A" and punch 6 holes in the bottom of each one. Use a nail and hammer to do this. Cut 2 pieces of paper into circles so they just fit inside the 2 cans. Cover the holes in the bottom of each can with a circle of paper. Next use a balance at school or in a grocery store to find the weight of each can with the circle of paper in it.

Fill one can with dry, sandy soil; fill the other can with dry, non-sandy soil. Find the weight of each can of soil. Now put a watch in one hand and a cup of water in the other hand. Pour the water into one of the cans of soil; find the time it takes for the water to start coming out the holes in the bottom of the can. Also do this with the second can of soil. Record the times in the table.

Next, add a lot of water to each can until the soils are completely soaked. Let each can of soil drip and drain for about an hour. After an hour, re-weigh each can of wet soil. Save the cans of wet soil for experiment "D."

The water that drips through the soil is pulled through by gravity. It is called *gravitational water*. Some water stays in the soil after the gravitational water has dripped out; this water is held by the soil against the pull of gravity. This is the water held by the soil at *field capacity*. It is the most water a soil can normally hold. Soil at field capacity has air in it, too. Can you think of a way to make soil have more water in it than it can hold at field capacity? Does this ever happen in a farmer's field?

10. Length of time for water to start coming out the bottom	________seconds	________seconds
11. Weight of can, paper and dry soil	________	________
12. Weight of empty can and circle of paper	________	________
13. Weight of dry soil (item 11 – item 12)	________	________
14. Weight of can, paper and wet soil	________	________
15. Weight of wet soil (item 14 – item 12)	________	________
16. Weight of water in wet soil (item 15 – item 13)	________	________
17. Percent water held by soil at field capacity $\left(\frac{\text{item 16 x 100}}{\text{item 13}}\right)$	________%	________%

Experiment "D"

D. Use the two cans of wet soil from experiment "C" for this experiment. Soak 12 seeds of corn, sunflower, or beans in a glass of water for an hour. Then plant the soaked seeds in each can of wet soil. To do this, dig 6 small holes in each can of soil; put one seed in each hole and cover the seeds with the wet soil. The seeds should be 1/4 to 1/2 inch below the soil surface. Put the cans in a warm place but not in direct sunlight or on a radiator.

Water the cans of soil each day or two. Keep watering the seedlings until they are about 3 inches high. One can may have fewer seedlings than the other can has. If this happens, cut off enough seedlings in the can that has more seedlings so both cans have the same number. Water the soil in both cans thoroughly.

Now record the date; do not add any water to either can of soil for the rest of this experiment. Let the seedlings continue to grow; look at the seedlings each day. Record the dates on which the seedlings in each can start to wilt or droop. Record the dates in the table. Use these dates to find the number of days it took for the seedlings in each can to droop.

Dig up the plant roots in each can of soil. Write in the table which can of soil has more roots in it.

Feel the soil from each can. Does it feel dry? Have the plants used up ALL the water in the soil? How could you find if the soils still have water in them, even though the plants wilted? Try it!

18. Date watering of soil was stopped	________	________
19. Date seedlings wilted	________	________
20. Number of days for seedlings to wilt (item 19 – item 18)	________	________
21. Soil with more roots	________	________

Summing Up! Look at the results of your experiments with sandy and non-sandy soils. Make a list of the differences between the two soils. For example, which soil holds more water at field capacity? Which soil has more clay and silt particles? Can you explain why plants in one soil wilted sooner than plants in the other soil? Does the soil with more sand hold more water? How does one soil hold more water than another soil? Which of the two soils would be easier to plow? Which of the two soils would have to be irrigated more often? Why do plants grow well in a soil that has air in it?

3. Can you grow plants without soil? You will need several chemicals for this experiment. They can usually be bought at a pharmacy, or a high-school chemistry teacher may be able to supply you with the chemicals.

First, get three quarts of sand from a sandpile. Put the sand in a large, clean pail and flood it with water. Stir it rapidly and pour off the cloudy water. Be careful not to pour off the sand! Add fresh water, stir again, and pour off the cloudy water. Keep doing this until the water is clear and is not even slightly cloudy.

Now get three quart-sized, waxed-paper drinking cups. The size used for malted milks or king-size drinks of soda pop is just right. With a nail, poke one hole in the center of the bottom of each cup. Put 2 or 3 pieces of paper towel or newspaper inside the cup. The paper should cover the hole and should lie flat on the bottom of the cup.

Pour the wet, clean sand into the cups. Do this carefully so that the paper over the hole is not moved. Fill the cups with sand to 1/2 inch from the top. Pour some water into each cup; this settles the sand. You may have to add a little more sand; but do not pack the sand into the cups with your hand. If everything has been done right, clear water should drip out the bottom of each cup when you pour water on the sand. If sand comes out the bottom of the cup, empty the cup and start over.

Soak 18 seeds (tomato, bean, radish, corn, sunflower, cantaloupe, or watermelon seeds work fine for this experiment) in a glass of water for an hour. Then put 6 soaked seeds in each of the 3 cups of sand. The seeds should be about 1/2 inch deep. Label the cups as follows:

Cup #1 water
Cup #2 all nutrients
Cup #3 deficient nutrient

Set the cups on a tray or in a pan. Put them in a warm place, but not in direct sunlight or on a radiator.

Now you should start making the nutrient solutions. If you have a balance, some gram weights, and a metric cylinder, use the correct number of grams and milliliters to make the solutions. Otherwise, use kitchen measuring spoons and cups.

Make the following "stock solutions" of the chemicals. Put each stock solution in a clean drinking glass; label each glass with the proper capital letter.

Preparation of Stock Solutions

Stock Solution	Chemical	Amount of chemical used and amount of water it is dissolved in
A	Calcium nitrate $Ca(NO_3)_2$	Dissolve 12 grams (1 level tablespoon) of the chemical in 50 milliliters (2 ounces) of water.
B	Potassium nitrate KNO_3	Dissolve 5 grams (1¼ teaspoons) of the chemical in 50 milliliters (2 ounces) of water.
C	Magnesium sulfate $MgSO_4$	Dissolve 5 grams (1½ teaspoons) of the chemical in 20 milliliters (5 teaspoons) of water.
D	Potassium dihydrogen phosphate KH_2PO_4	Dissolve 1.5 grams (¼ teaspoon) of the chemical in 10 milliliters (2½ teaspoons) of water.
E	Calcium phosphate $Ca(H_2PO_4)_2$	Dissolve 1 grams (¼ teaspoon) of the chemical in 400 milliliters (14 ounces) of water.
F	Potassium sulfate K_2SO_4	Dissolve 5 grams (1 teaspoon) of the chemical in 60 milliliters (2 ounces) of water.
G	Calcium sulfate $CaSO_4$	Dissolve 1 grams (1 teaspoon) of the chemical in 600 milliliters (21 ounces) of water.
H	Iron solution Fe solution	Scrape some iron rust into 1 teaspoon of vinegar; let stand for an hour; stir before using.

Use tap water to make up these and all other solutions. The tap water contains enough of the elements needed in very small amounts (boron, copper, chlorine, molybdenum, zinc, cobalt, and manganese).

Now get three containers of ½ gallon size. Empty half-gallon milk containers are just right (they can be glass or waxed-paper milk cartons). Rinse the containers with water several times. Label them as follows:

#1 Water
#2 All nutrients
#3 Deficient nutrient

In doing the following things be very careful to keep the utensils very clean. Rinse the measuring glass and spoon with fresh water each time just before you use them.

Fill container #1 with tap water.

Put the following things in container #2. Mix them in the order given:

1972 milliliters (2 quarts) of water;
10 milliliters (2½ teaspoons) of stock solution A;
10 milliliters (2½ teaspoons) of stock solu- B;
4 milliliters (1 teaspoon) of stock solution C;
2 milliliters (½ teaspoon) of stock solution D;
2 milliliters (½ teaspoon) of stock solution H.

Put the following in container #3. Mix them in the order given:

1457 milliliters (1½ quarts) of water;
1 milliliter (¼ teaspoon) of stock solution C;
100 milliliters (3½ ounces) of stock solution E;
40 milliliters (3 tablespoons and 1 teaspoon) of stock solution F;
400 milliliters (14 ounces) of stock solution G;
2 milliliters (½ teaspoon) of stock solution H.

The glasses of stock solutions (A to H) may be discarded now. If you want to save them for use again, put them in clean bottles with clean, tight-fitting caps.

Slowly pour about 50 milliliters (two to three ounces) of tap water on each of the three cups of sprouting seeds every day. Sometimes the pots may need more water; always add enough water to make solution drip out the bottom of each pot. When the seedlings grow above the sand surface, the pots of plants should be put where they will get direct sunlight a few hours each day.

When the seedlings are about 1 inch tall, pinch off all except two of the seedlings in each pot. Now the pots of plants are ready to be given the different nutrient treatments.

It is best to shake the solution in each container just before it is used.

Pour 50 to 75 milliliters (two to three ounces) from container #1 into cup #1.

Pour 50 to 75 milliliters (two to three ounces) of solution from container #2 into pot #2.

Pour 50 to 75 milliliters (two to three ounces) of solution from container #3 into pot #3.

Each day, for the next 20 to 30 days, pour solution from the proper container into the proper pot of plants. Use at least 50 to 75 milliliters (2 to 3 ounces) each time, but always add enough so solution drips out the bottom of each pot.

You may have an accident and pour a solution into the wrong pot. If this happens, slowly pour about a quart of water into the pot that got the wrong solution. This will flush out the wrong solution. Then pour the right solution into the pot. It is best to be careful and avoid such accidents!

Record the date on which you first use solutions #1, 2, and 3 to water the plants. Also find the heights (in centimeters or inches) of both seedlings in each of the 3 pots on this date. Record the heights in the table.

Find the heights of each plant every 3 days until the experiment is ended. Also record any observations of the plants: discoloration of leaves, dead spots on leaves, general vigor of plant, size of leaves, diameter of stem, etc.

At the end of the experiment (20 to 30 days after first using the solutions), do these things:

A. Carefully wash the sand away from the roots in each pot.

Record the general appearance of the roots. Find the total fresh weight of the roots from each pot. Use a balance at school or the scales in a grocery.

B. Find the total fresh weight of the stems and leaves from each pot.

TREATMENT OF PLANTS

	#1 — Water		#2 — All Nutrients		#3 — Deficient Nutrient	
Date	Height	Appearance	Height	Appearance	Height	Appearance
1.						
2.						
3.						
4.						
5.						
6.						
7.						
8.						
9.						
10.						
Roots: Appearance						
Weight						
Weight of Stems & Leaves:						

Try graphing the average heights of the plants from each of the three pots. The average height of plants in each pot is found this way: add the heights of the two plants together; divide this total by 2 (which is the number of plants in a pot). The graph for this experiment is on page 115.

Which nutrient used in large amounts by plants was missing from the solution in container #3? How do the cells of plants use this nutrient? Can you explain the appearance of a plant not getting enough of this nutrient on the basis of how the nutrient is used by plants?

What nutrients did pot #1 NOT receive?

Can you explain why the plants in each pot grew as they did?

Can you explain the shapes of the 3 curves in the graph? Why did the average height of plants in one pot stop increasing so early in the experiment? Can you tell by just looking at the 3 curves in your graph, which pot of plants grew the fastest?

This is not a trip for softies!

ADVENTURE 6

A Trip Through The Plumbing Pipes

CIRCULATION

Here we go, through the pit of this *xylem pipe!*

A Trip Through The Plumbing Pipes

Do you like to ride roller-coasters or fast elevators in buildings? Do you dream of being a space pilot and being shot high into the sky in a rocket? Or perhaps you would like to fly through the clouds in a fast jet airplane? Well, if these things sound like fun to you, come with me! I'll take you on an adventure that you'll never forget! It's not a trip for softies, though! You will get bruised and banged around; you may even break a bone or two. And once we get started, there will be no turning back. So if you are chicken and afraid of getting a little scratched, please stay at home!

You still want to go? Wonderful! I knew you would want to explore the unknown and be thrilled by this new adventure.

We are going on a trip through the many plumbing pipes of a large tree in your neighborhood. Here is a map to show you where we are going. To help protect you from the dangers of this trip, you will need to wear this football uniform. It has extra padding in it to give you added protection. Be sure to put this football helmet on tight, too. You won't want to get knocked out during the trip! Now put this rubber suit over your football uniform and helmet; it's like deep-sea divers use and will keep your clothing from getting waterlogged. Finally, here is a pair of unbreakable goggles. The goggles will protect your eyes from fast-moving molecules, edges of cells, and various moving objects. One last thing; tie this piece of rope around your waist. I'll tie the other end around my waist. Then we'll be sure to stay together, just as if we were mountain climbers. Now I think we're ready to go. Let's walk over to that large tree and begin our adventure!

In order to see the plumbing pipes of plants from the inside, we will have to use the reducing pills again. I brought along 20 pills for each of us. That will give us 10 hours to make the trip. A tour of the plumbing pipes usually takes several hours, and I don't want us to return to normal size before it's over! Are you ready? I am too. Swallow all 20 reducing pills and follow. . .me. .e. . .e. . .e.

We will begin our trip in a root hair of this tree. But it'll take us a while to burrow through the soil down to the roots and root hairs. So let's go! Watch out for earthworms and other animals! Remember, we're smaller than the cells in those creatures. If an insect stepped on you, it would crush you! And if an earthworm should slide past you, it would probably smash you against the pieces of sand and clay in the soil!

There is a lot of air and space in this soil, so we have plenty of passage ways and tunnels to walk through. See how dark it is getting? Just like in caves. But don't worry, I brought along a flashlight. Be careful not to let those sharp edges of the soil particles rip your rubber suit! Every particle of sand and clay is covered with a layer of water. The plant roots use that water if they happen to grow into it. But the water layer makes it dangerous for you and me. Sometimes the water covers up a very sharp edge of sand and you can't see it. So be careful!

Ah! I think I see a root up ahead. Yes, there it is!

All we have to do now is find a root hair. If I shine the flashlight over that way, maybe we'll see some. Sure enough, I see a few hundred of them. Let's go into this one. It seems healthy and busy taking in water; that means a quick journey through the root hair for us!

I'll push these fibers of the cell wall apart so we can enter. Things will happen fast once we go into the root hair, so be prepared. And watch out for flying objects! When we get in the main pipes where water is going up to the leaves, be very careful. We will be caught in a stream of water moving about 10 feet an hour. That doesn't sound very fast, but it is. Remember, we are very much reduced in size; we're one millionth our normal height. Moving 10 feet an hour while we are this small size will be like going 3000 miles an hour when we are normal size! That is pretty fast, and we won't have anything to protect us except our football uniform and helmet!

Here we go! Follow me into this root hair. The cytoplasm of this root hair is streaming and will carry us to the other end of the hair. Watch out for that nucleus! Whew! That was close! The end of the root hair is just ahead. Now we'll push our way through the end of the root hair and into the main part of the root. There is a lot of space between the cells of the root for us to go through. The space is filled with water, though, so we'll have to swim. Isn't this fun? It's better than skin-diving along the ocean shore!

The plumbing pipes are near the center of the root. As we get near them, you'll feel the water current get stronger. Can you feel the current pulling you along now? I can! In a few moments the current will get very swift. It will be worse than going over Niagara Falls! Then we'll be swished along the stream of water right into the plumbing pipes. Watch out, though. Each plumbing pipe has small holes in its side called *pits*. Make sure you go through the same pit I do! Otherwise the rope between us will get us fouled. Get set; up . . we . . .go . . .o . . . o . . . . o

Now we'll push the fibers of the cell wall apart so we can crawl into the root hair.

Up . . . we . . . gooo . . . o . . . o . . . !

Swish . . . . Crunch . . . . Ohhhhh . . . .

Here, let me help you get your wind back! You took a nasty bump when you came out the end of the plumbing pipe we were in. Any bones broken? None? Good! Did that seem like a long trip to you? It didn't seem long to me, but it did seem like being in a hurricane, tornado, earthquake, and falling from an airplane all at the same time! It took us about three hours to go up 30 feet in the plumbing pipe. That pipe we were in is part of the *xylem*. The xylem pipes carry water to all parts of the plant. Xylem pipes are simply long tubes from the roots up the stem to every branch and leaf. After you get your wind back, take a look down there. See, through that stomate of the leaf we're resting in? Can you see the lady down there? She's hanging up some clothes to dry. I bet she would never guess that we're up here inside this leaf watching her!

See the swarm of flea-like objects going out that stomate? They are the water molecules that swished us up through the xylem pipes. Now they have evaporated from the cells of the leaf we are sitting in. After they evaporate, they swarm through the stomate out to the air around the leaf. Botanists call this evaporation of water from cells *transpiration*. Dixon, an Irish botanist, found that transpiration pulls water up the plumbing pipes of a tree. That's how we got up the tree, too. Transpiration pulled us up along with the water.

We can see water molecules going out the *stomate* of this leaf. It's called *transpiration*.

Are you ready to finish our trip? We have to go back down some plumbing pipes to the roots. The pipes we will use for this part of our trip are called *phloem* pipes. I see some phloem over there, in that leaf vein. The veins of leaves have both kinds of plumbing pipes, xylem and phloem. Xylem carries water and minerals to the leaf. Phloem carries sugar to other parts of the plant that can't make their own food or are storing food. Roots can't make their own food, so if we ride in the phloem pipes they will take us to the roots. O.K., let's go!

This phloem cell we're in is a living cell. See how long it is and how fast things are moving through it? Both ends of these phloem cells have holes in them. The sugar made in the leaf cells moves through this cell, then through the holes into the next cell, and so on until the sugar gets to where it is used. Of course, the sugar is mixed with water and isn't crystals of sugar like you put on your breakfast cereal! See that swarm of small ball-like objects coming toward us, the ones that look like two marbles stuck together? They are sugar molecules. Millions, billions, trillions of them! They will push us through the phloem cells down to the roots.

The holes of the phloem cell we are riding in are just ahead. Be sure to follow me through the same hole! You can tell we aren't moving as fast as we did going up in the xylem. It will take us a few hours to get back down to the roots. If you want to, why don't you rest and take a nap? I'll see that you get through the holes at the end of each phloem cell. It's been a hard trip, and you need the rest! I'll wake you up when we get down to the roots. But don't snore! The noise might hurt the phloem cells, and then we would be stranded inside this tree!

Time to wake up! You really were sound asleep. It took us about six hours to come down the phloem and you never woke up once! We're almost down to the root tip now. Come on, I'll lead the way out to the edge of the root. Be very careful, though. We don't want to get caught in the stream of water going into the xylem! Then we'd be pulled up the xylem to the leaves again. That wouldn't be so bad, but our time is running out; the effect of the reducing pills will be wearing off soon. If you happened to be at the top of the tree just when you returned to normal size, you might fall out of the tree! I don't think you would want to fall 30 feet out of a tree!

Be careful now, and hang on to the thread-like fibers of the cell walls. That will help you move against the stream of water going into the xylem pipes. It's going to be like moving upstream against a very swift current, so hang on tight!

Ah, now the current isn't so swift. We're getting near the outside edge of the root where the root hairs are. They're just ahead of us now. We'll rest there and wait until the effect of the reducing pills wears off. Then as we get back to normal size, we'll burst out of the root and through the soil. It won't hurt us because we have this football uniform on. It'll just make a little mess in your yard where we come up through the soil. Be sure to keep your mouth closed, though, when we return to normal size. Otherwise you will get a mouthful of soil!

I think the effect of the reducing pills is wearing off now. Brace yourself! Hope you enjoyed this ad . . vent . . . u . . . r . . r

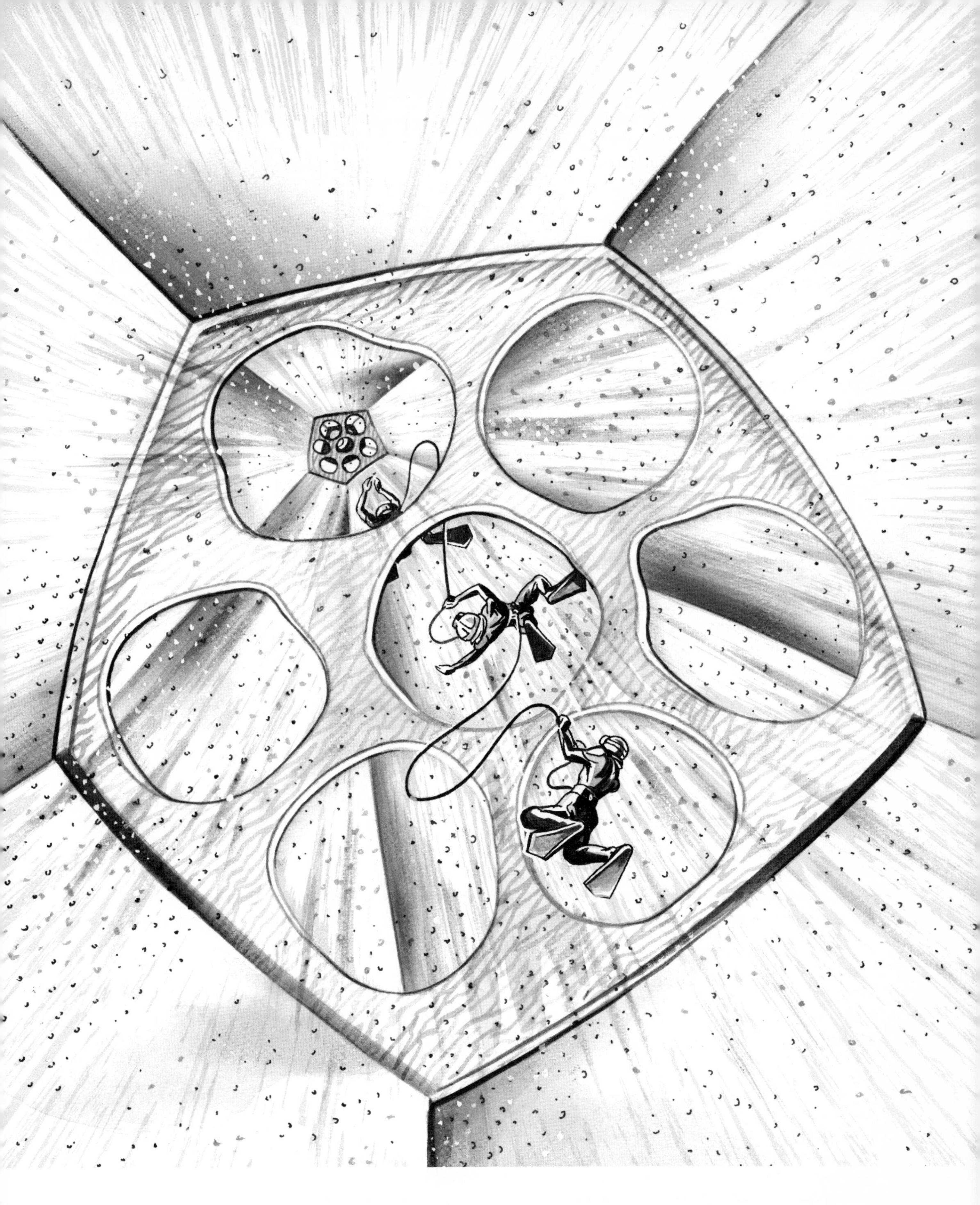

Here we go through this *phloem* pipe. The sugar molecules will push us.

Things to Do and Think About

1. Does water really evaporate from leaves? Find a large polyethylene bag with no holes or cuts in it. Fully inflated, the bag should be one foot or more in diameter. Next pick out a branch on a shrub or tree; the branch should have *many* leaves on it. Without ripping the bag, put the bag over the branch; tie the open end of the bag tight around the main stem of the branch. Use a piece of wire or string to tie the bag. The bag should now form a "balloon" around the branch.

Record the time. Wait an hour or more. Then untie the bag and carefully remove it from the branch. Do this without spilling any of the water that has collected in the bag. Pour the water from the bag into a kitchen measuring cup. Record the amount of water. Now count the number of leaves on the part of the branch that was inside the bag. Estimate the number of leaves on the whole plant. Record your notes in the table and do the calculations.

1. Time at start of experiment ________
2. Time at end of experiment ________
3. Length of experiment in minutes (item 2 minus item 1) ________
4. Amount of water collected ________
5. Number of leaves inside bag ________
6. Amount of water lost each minute by all the leaves (item 4 divided by item 3) ________
7. Amount of water lost each minute by one leaf (item 6 divided by item 5) ________
8. Estimated number of leaves on whole plant ________
9. Amount of water lost each minute by the whole plant (item 7 multiplied by item 8) ________
10. Amount of water lost in an 8-hour day by the whole plant (item 9 multiplied by 60 minutes multiplied by 8 hours) ________

This experiment can also be done with a bag over a corn plant, tobacco plant, branch of a cotton plant, or any large plant. Try it!

How much water would collect in the bag if the experiment were done at night? Try it and see!

2. Does water really move inside the xylem plumbing pipes? For this experiment you will need: a fresh leafy stalk of celery; red or blue food coloring; glass of water; and a knife.

Use several drops of food coloring to color very darkly a glass of water. Then make a clean, diagonal cut across the stalk of celery; see the diagram. The cut must be at an angle across the stalk. *Immediately* after you cut the celery, stand the celery in the glass of colored water. Put the set-up in direct sunlight and watch it for the next few minutes. If you made a clean, diagonal cut and did not let any air bubbles get into the plumbing pipes, things should happen within an hour.

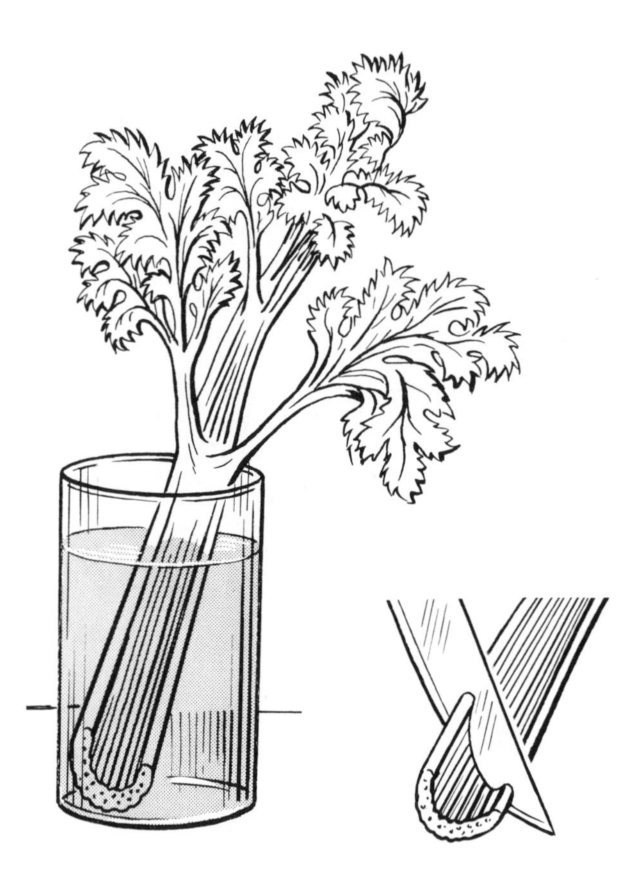

When the celery leaves have become colored, remove the stalk from the glass of colored water. Make two more cuts; one cut across the stalk of celery and the other cut up and down the stalk. Look at the cut surfaces of the stalk. What parts are colored? Did the food coloring spread into the leaves? How did the food coloring move up the celery?

Take another fresh stalk of celery, and do this experiment again; but this time find out how fast the food coloring moves up the celery stalk. You can figure out how to do this. Figure out how fast it moves up the celery, in inches or centimeters per hour.

What would happen if you placed the set-up in a dark room instead of in direct sunlight? Would the coloring still move up the stalk? Would it move as fast? Would it move in the same parts of the celery stalk? Try it and see!

Would wind make the food coloring move faster or slower? What would happen if you cut off all the leaves of the celery stalk at the beginning of the experiment? Try it!

Put the set-up inside a polyethylene bag in sunlight. Does this change the time it takes for the coloring to move up the stalk? Can you explain why?

3. What part of the seedling has food for use by the seedling? Get a quart of clean sand from a sandpile. Also get two small waxed-paper drinking cups. With a nail, poke one hole in the bottom of each cup. Put a small piece of paper over the hole in each cup. Then nearly fill both cups with sand. Pour some water into each cup to settle the sand; no sand should come out the bottom of the cup. Put 20 seeds of sunflower or bean in a glass of water for an hour. Then plant 10 soaked seeds in each cup of sand. The seeds should be planted about 1/2 inch deep and you should space them uniformly in the cup.

Put the two cups on a tray in a warm place, but not in direct sunlight or on a radiator. Water them when the sand at the top starts to feel dry. When the seedlings start to rise above the sand, do these things:

A. Do nothing to 1 cup of seedlings.
B. Each seedling has 2 cotyledons. The cotyledons are the thick, roundish, leaf-like objects that come out of the seed. They are covered by the seed coats just before they unfold above the sand. With a knife, carefully cut off the cotyledons (seed leaves) from all the seedlings in the second cup. Try to do this without uprooting the seedlings. When you cut them off, be careful not to cut the young leaves and stem that are starting to grow between the cotyledons.

Now the 2 cups should look like this:

Let the seedlings grow for 2 or 3 weeks. Give them water every day. Which seedlings grow larger and are healthier? Can you explain why? How does the food get from one place to another in the seedling?

After 2 or 3 weeks, remove 5 seedlings (including roots) from each cup. Weigh all 5 seedlings from Cup A at the same time. Do the same for the 5 seedlings from Cup B. Which group of seedlings weigh the most? Are the heaviest seedlings the ones that look the healthiest?

4. How much water moves through a plant? Things needed for this experiment are:

- sharp knife
- glass tube, about 12 inches long and about 1/4 inch in diameter
- rubber tubing, about 15 inches long; it should fit tightly over the end of the glass tube
- large dish pan or pail

Wet the end of the glass tube with water, and fit it into the rubber tubing. Slide the rubber tubing one inch over the end of the glass tube.

Fill the dishpan with water. Now go outside and cut a branch from a shrub or tree. The stem of the branch should be about 1/4 inch in diameter at the place where you cut it. The branch should have *many* leaves on it. After cutting the branch from the plant, QUICKLY put the cut end of the branch in the pan of water. QUICKLY make a second cut, diagonally, about 2 inches from the end, with the stem and knife under water.

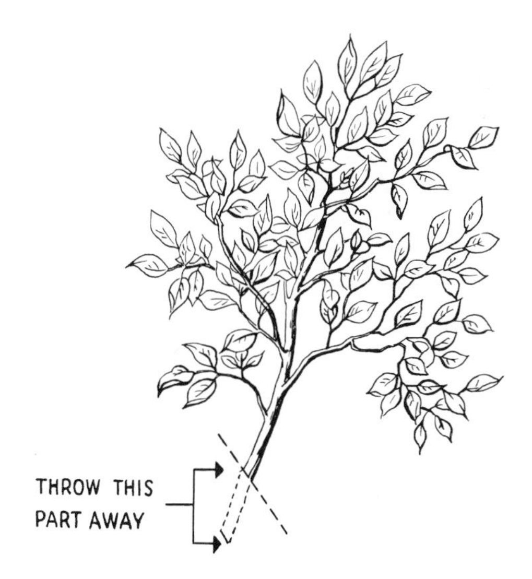

Now put the end of the rubber tubing in the pan of water. Fit the rubber tubing tightly over the cut end of the branch. Fill the rubber tubing and glass tube with water. Hold the tubing and let the branch hang upside down; tap the side of the rubber tube to make sure no air bubbles are caught in it. Any air bubbles inside it will rise and come out the end of the glass tube.

Now mount the tubing and branch upright so the rubber tube bends into a U-shape (see drawing below). No water should leak out the place where the rubber tubing covers the end of the branch. If it does, start over with a little wider branch.

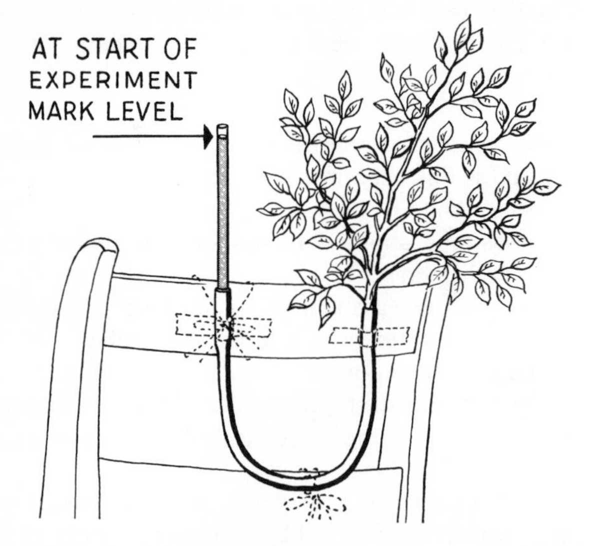

After you put the set-up in position, mark the level of water in the glass tube. Use a wax crayon or piece of tape to do this. Also record the time. Put the set-up in direct sunlight. As the branch transpires water from the leaves and stems, the level of water in the glass tube will go down.

After one hour, mark the new level of water in the glass tube. Use a ruler to find the distance between the first level and the second level of water. Also find the diameter of the opening in the glass tube. Record these things in the table and try the calculations.

Now move the set-up (botanists call it a *potometer)* to a different condition. Try putting the set-up in a sunny, windy place. Or you can put it in a dark hallway. Record the time at the beginning, the level of water at the beginning, etc., as you did before. After doing this, try other conditions of sunlight, wind, and shade. See if you can figure out why the branch uses different amounts of water when it is in different conditions.

You will have to refill the glass tube with water every now and then. Do not let any air get into the rubber tubing or into the branch. The air will clog the plumbing pipes; then you will have to start over with a new branch.

After you have made several measurements with your potometer, try this experiment. Take some vaseline, oleomargarine, or chicken grease, and smear a thin layer of it over the top and bottom sides of all the leaves of the branch in your potometer. Then put the potometer in a sunny place. Record the time and level of water in the tube. Make the measurements and calculations as you did before. Try to explain the results that you get.

Table of Data from Experiment 4

	Test 1	Test 2	Test 3	Test 4
1. Condition (sunny, windy, shady, etc.)				
2. Time at start of experiment				
3. Time at end of experiment				
4. Length of experiment (item 3 minus item 2)				
5. Distance water level dropped during experiment				
6. Diameter of opening of glass tube				
7. Volume of water lost by plant during experiment (see "hint" below)				
8. Volume of water lost by plant in 1 hour (see "hint" below)				

Hints: The volume of a cylinder is equal to:

$$\frac{\text{diameter}}{2} \times \frac{\text{diameter}}{2} \times \frac{22}{7} \times \text{length of cylinder}$$

Both the diameter and length of cylinder must be measured in the same units. If you know how much water was lost during the experiment and how long (in minutes) the experiment was, then you can figure out how much water would be lost in 1 minute. Knowing how many minutes there are in an hour, you can now figure out the amount of water lost by the plant in 1 hour.

ADVENTURE 7
New And Bigger Cells
GROWTH

We're standing on the bud of the stem . . .

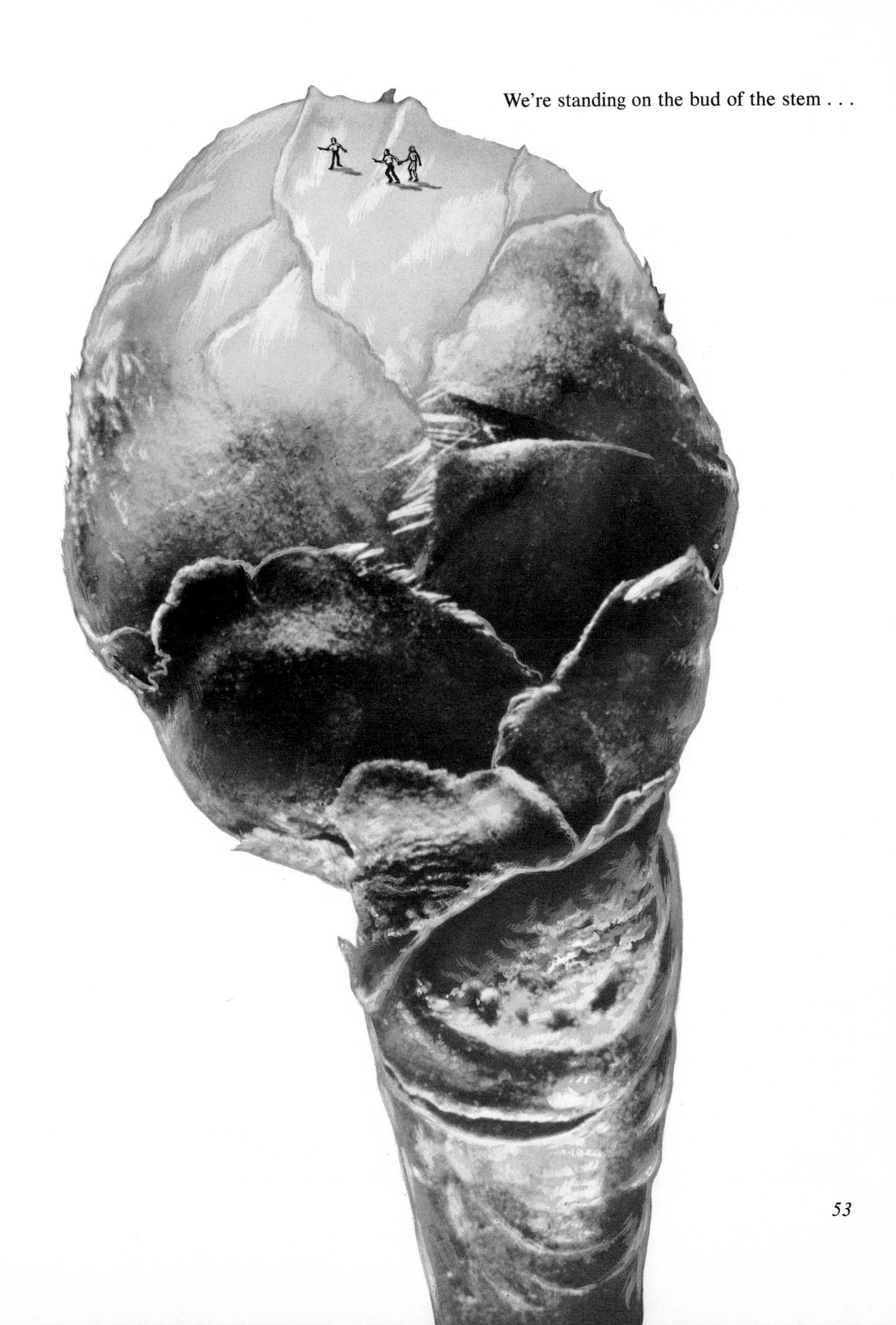

New And Bigger Cells

HAVE YOU ever watched something grow? Perhaps you watched your baby sister or brother grow. Perhaps you watched the growth of a tree or some flowers that you helped to plant in your yard. Perhaps you watched a pet dog, cat, fish, or bird grow. What do all these things do when they grow? Do they all get larger? It doesn't matter what is growing—baby sister, a plant, a pet—they all get larger. Have you ever seen a plant or animal grow smaller? No! Things always grow larger.

How do plants and animals grow larger? Well, we know that living things are made of cells. This means that when plants and animals grow, their cells do the growing. But how do cells grow? Come with me! I'll show you some growing cells and then you can see for yourself how they do it. First, we'll have to find some cells that are growing. See that bush out there, toward the street? Where in that bush would you expect to find cells that are growing? Do you remember what I showed you in our first adventure about where roots and stems come from? Let me refresh your memory. We found that roots grow more roots, and stems grow more stems. This means that we should be able to find growing cells in the tips of roots and stems. Since stems are easier for us to get into than roots, let's go inside the stem tip of that bush and watch its cells grow! Here are a couple of reducing pills for you. Now hold on to the tip of the same stem that I do, and swallow the pills. In a few moments we'll meet each other on the stem tip of this bush! See . . . you . . . . the . . r . . e .

Look at all the tiny leaves around us! We are standing on the *bud* of the stem. These tiny leaves are called *bud leaves*. They will grow up to be normal leaves several hundred times larger than they are now. But let's not watch them grow; let's go inside the bud and see how the stem grows! Follow me and I'll lead the way into the cells of this stem tip. As we walk along, listen carefully and you can hear some scratchy sounds. Those sounds are made by the bud leaves scraping against each other as they grow and unfold!

Look at this round surface we're standing on; it looks like a round mountain top! It's the very tip of the stem. New cells are being made a few cells underneath us. That's where we are going now. It'll just take us a while to force our way through these cells of the stem tip to get there.

Here we are! You can see that these cells are much smaller and more like cubes than the cells we visited on our other adventures. That's because they haven't grown in size yet! Some of these cubical cells never will get any larger. They'll just go on making more cells. Oh, I'm sorry! I forgot to tell you that cells make more cells. It's called *cell division*. This isn't the kind of division you have in arithmetic. In cell division, when one cell divides, two new cells are formed. The cell that divided becomes the two new cells. But each of the two new cells is about as large as the parent cell that formed it! It's sort of like cutting a cake into two pieces, except the two pieces grow as large as the first piece of cake while you cut the cake! One cell divides into two cells, and the two new cells are just as large as the first cell! This all sounds pretty tricky, doesn't it? Well, watch for yourself! The cell we're standing in is starting to make two new cells, right now. Watch closely, though, or you'll miss all the fun! Things happen fast when a cell divides.

. . . Now we're on the tip of the stem inside the bud.

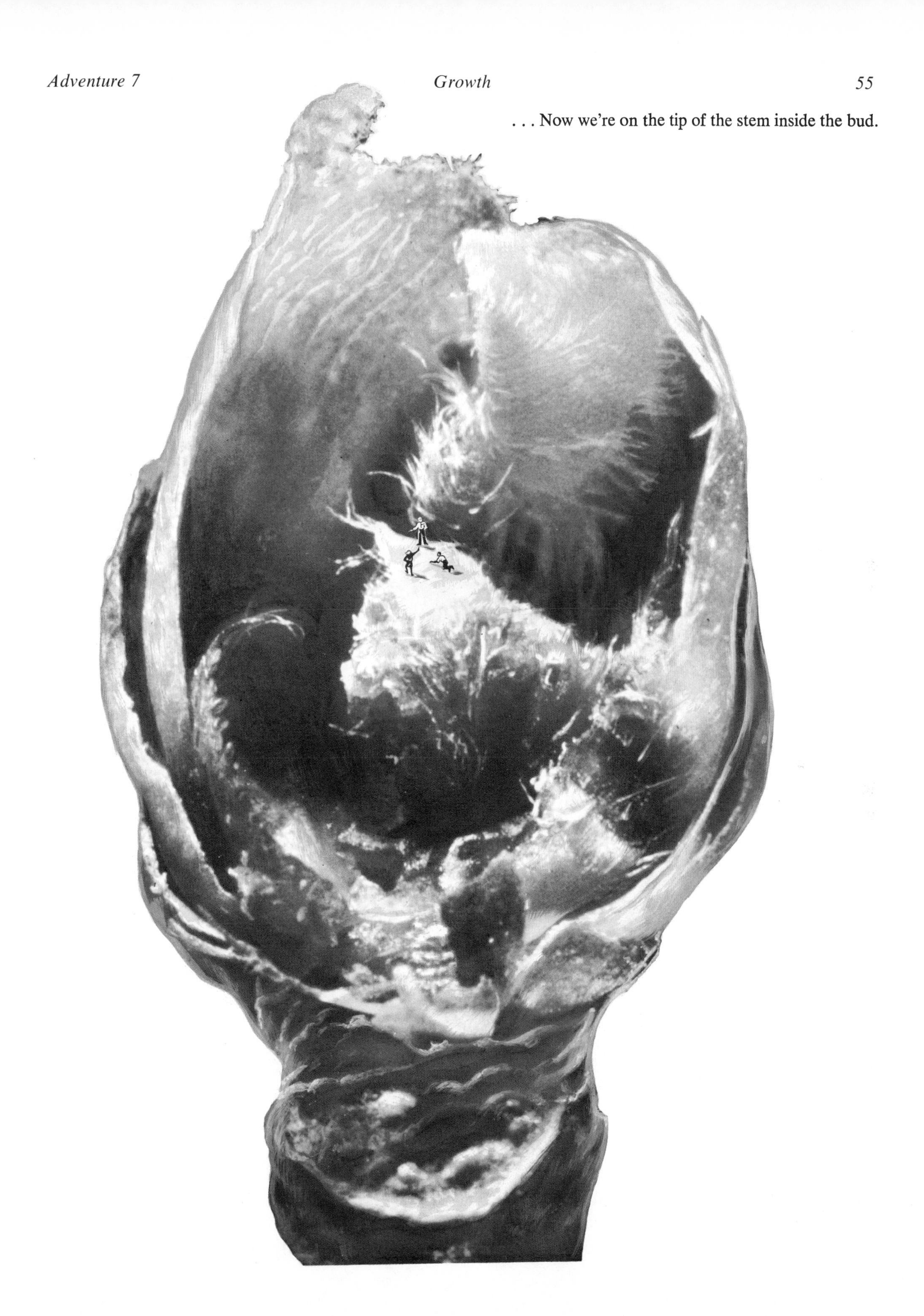

That's the nucleus in front of us. Can you see those long, twisted strings inside the nucleus, the ones that look like long chains of beads? Those are the chromosomes in the nucleus. Now take a close look at the chromosome just in front of us. Watch it do something that no magician has ever done. That chromosome will start making a partner! And the partner will look just like the chromosome that caused it to be made! We won't be able to see exactly how each chromosome makes its partner; no one knows just how that happens. But it does! See that chromosome twisting and turning? And now it has chemicals crowded around it that are beginning to look just like another chromosome. And there it is! The chromosome has made a partner. Now you can't tell which one is the partner, because they both look exactly alike! I wish I could tell you how that chromosome made a partner; until a scientist discovers how it is done it will have to remain one of the great mysteries of nature. Keep your eyes on the chromosomes; you'll see them get thicker and shorter. See!

Now the pairs of chromosome partners will stay side by side for a little while, but not for long. Things will begin to happen fast, now. We better stand back near the side of the cell where we won't be in the way. We could easily be smashed against the cell wall by one of the chromosomes when it starts to move!

Look at them now! All the pairs of chromosome partners are lined up across the center of the cell. Watch out! Boy, that was close! You almost got caught in the *spindle fibers!* I should have warned you about the *spindle*. When the pairs of chromosomes move toward the center of the cell, a spindle is formed. The spindle is made of several string-like fibers that stretch from each end of the cell to the chromosomes. One "string" or fiber attaches to one of the partners of chromosomes. Every chromosome has one fiber attached to it. Be careful! Don't get in the way! The spindle fibers will snap back very soon. Each fiber will pull the chromosome it is attached to. The chromosome will be pulled to the end of the cell. Look out! There they go! See how one chromosome partner is pulled to this end of the cell? There goes its partner to the other end of the cell! Now each end of the cell has the same kind of chromosomes. One partner is moved to each end of the cell. Count the number of chromosomes at each end of the cell. Did you count the same number at each end? Good! I wish I knew how the spindle fibers pull the chromosomes, but no one has discovered that yet. One thing you can be sure of; it takes a lot of energy to do all these things when a cell divides. That's one reason only healthy plants and animals grow fast. It also tells us why babies sleep and eat so much; they're all worn out from growing so fast!

While we were talking, the last step of cell division happened. See that wall over there, the one across the center of the cell? Surprised, aren't you? It wasn't there a minute ago! That wall across the cell was made just after the two groups of chromosomes were pulled apart. Now there are two new cells where before there was only one! We are standing in one cell; you can see parts of the other cell through that new cell wall.

We have watched one of the great marvels of nature: cell division! That is one way a plant or animal grows; it makes more cells. And that makes the organism larger. Now let's see a second way that cells grow. I think that cell next door to us is starting to grow the second way. Watch it awhile and you will see how it's done.

Look carefully! Do you see the swarms of flea-like water molecules going into the cell? A special chemical has made the wall of that cell like bubble-gum. As the water goes

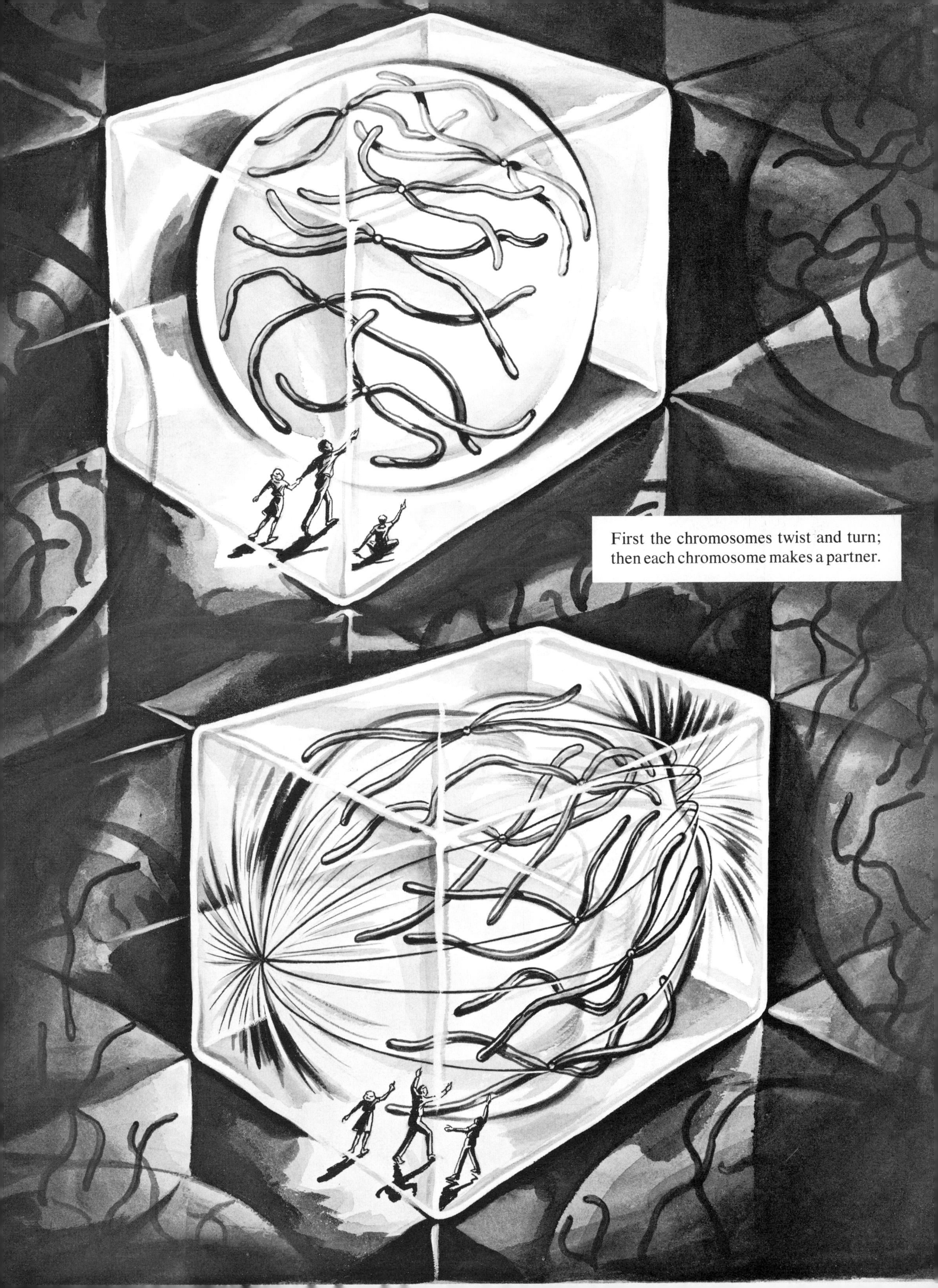

First the chromosomes twist and turn;
then each chromosome makes a partner.

Stand back! Chromosomes on the move! Now there are two cells!

into the cell, the cell gets larger; and this makes the cell wall get stretched. See! The cell is growing real long. It's the same as when you are chewing bubble-gum; you blow air into the gum to make a larger "bubble" and the gum gets stretched. Very quickly now the wall of that cell will stop stretching and that will stop the swarms of water molecules from going in. There, it's stopping now! The bubble-like cell has enlarged as far as it can. No more water is going into it to make it larger, either. It looks to me like the cell is about 10 times longer than it was before it started growing.

Things happened so fast I forgot to tell you about the special chemicals that make the cell wall stretch like bubble-gum. The chemicals are called *auxins*. Auxins are made by cells that are rapidly dividing. Then the auxins move down the stem to where cells are ready to enlarge. And then they cause the cells to grow longer. Auxins are very potent chemicals in plants. A small ball of auxins the size of a pinhead is enough chemical to start millions and billions of cells growing. Three men discovered auxins — two chemists and a botanist. The botanist, Dr. Fritz Went, discovered a way of measuring the effect of auxins on plants. The chemists, Dr. Kogl and Dr. Haagen-Smit, identified the first auxin.

Although botanists and chemists have identified and named several auxins, no one knows HOW auxins make cells grow. The person who discovers THAT will become world famous! It might be you!

Whoops! I can feel the effect of the reducing pills starting to wear off. We finished this adventure in the nick . . . of . . . time . . .

Things to Do and Think About

1. Buds for science and eating! Try experiment #1 of Adventure 1 if you haven't done it.

2. Making models of a cell dividing. Get two balls of clay of different colors. Break each of the balls of clay into 11 pieces and all the same size. Roll each piece between your hands until it forms a "snake" about two inches long. Now you should have 22 snakes, 11 of each color. The snakes are going to stand for chromosomes! Now get seven sheets of white paper about 8 x 11 inches in size. Do these things to each sheet of paper:

Sheet #1. Draw a circle in the middle of the paper; the circle should be about 6 inches in diameter. Take one "chromosome" of each color of clay; roll each one between your hands until it is real long (about 12 inches). Now lay these "long chromosomes" inside the circle:

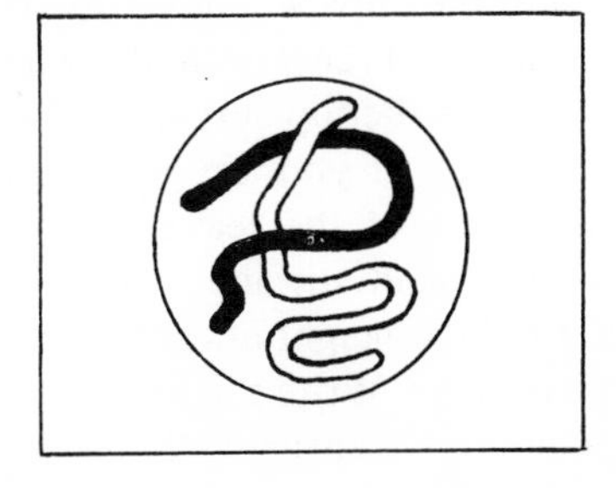

Sheet #2. Draw a circle in the middle of the paper; the circle should be the same size as you drew on sheet #1. Take two "chromosomes" of each color; roll each one between your hands until it is about 12 inches long. Take two of the same color and pinch them together in the middle so they look like this:

Lay the two pairs of "long chromosomes" inside the circle:

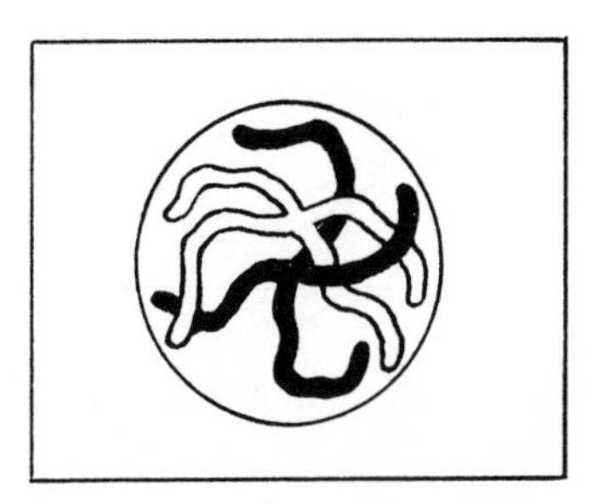

Sheet #3. Draw a circle in the middle of the paper; the circle should be the same size as before. Take two "chromosomes" of each color; pinch two of the same color together in the middle. Lay the two pairs of "chromosomes" inside the circle:

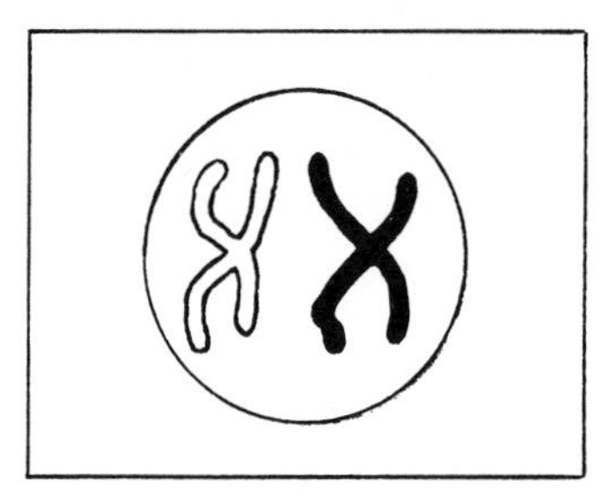

Sheet #4. Take two "chromosomes" of each color. Pinch two of the same color together in the middle. Lay the two pairs of "chromosomes" across the middle of the sheet of paper. Put a dot in the middle of each end of the paper; the dots should be about 1 inch from each end of the paper. Draw a line from each dot to the pinched part of each pair of "chromosomes:"

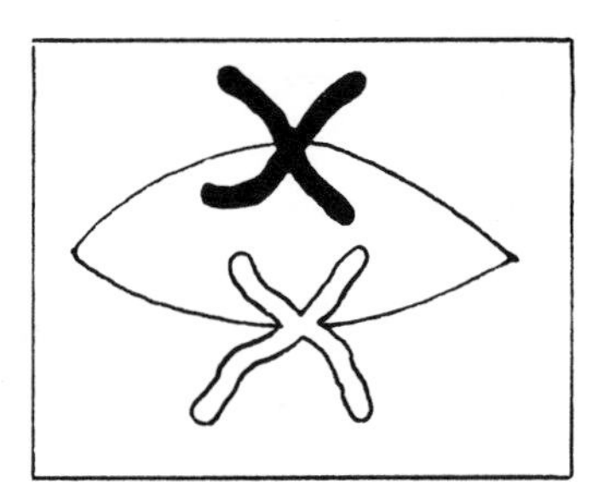

Sheet #5. Take two "chromosomes" of each color. Lay one of each color across the paper; the two "chromosomes" of the *same color* should be 2 or 3 inches from each other. Put a dot at each end of the paper as you did for sheet #4. Draw two lines from each dot to the two "chromosomes" nearest each dot:

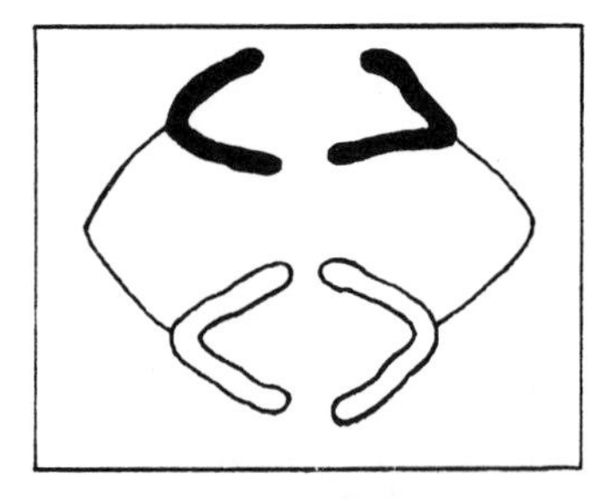

Sheet #6 and 7. Lay one sheet over the end of the other sheet; they should overlap about three inches. Use some glue or tape to stick them together. Now draw a circle on each sheet; the circles should be the same size as you used before. Take 2 "chromosomes" of each color; roll each one between your hands until it is about 12 inches long. Lay two of these "long snakes" inside each circle; each circle should have one "chromosome" of each color. Draw a line the width of the paper between the two circles:

A neat drawing of the steps of cell division makes a nice picture to hang on the wall in your bedroom or school classroom. Get a large sheet of white cardboard or heavy paper. Draw pictures on the cardboard in colors that look like the models you made with clay. Draw the pictures in the right order, and put a title at the top of the whole sheet.

Lay the models of cell division on a table; keep them in the same order in which you made them. Each sheet of paper stands for the cell that is dividing. The edge of the paper stands for the cell wall. The clay "snakes" stand for chromosomes. The two colors of clay help you to see where each chromosome partner goes when the cell divides. The circles you drew stand for the edge of the nucleus. The dots and lines from each end of the cell stand for the spindle fibers.

Does the cell at the beginning (sheet #1) look like the two cells at the end of cell division (sheets #6 and 7)? Are the two cells formed by cell division equal?

3. Watching plants grow. Get three waxed paper drinking cups all the same size. Poke 1 hole in the bottom of each cup; cover the hole with a piece of paper about the size of a 50c coin. Nearly fill each cup with clean sand. Put 18 seeds of bean, sunflower, tomato, or corn in a glass of water for an hour. Then plant 6 soaked seeds in each cup of sand. Space the seeds evenly and plant them about 1/2 inch deep in the sand.

Put the three cups on a tray in a warm, *dark* closet or cabinet. Water the cups whenever the sand starts to get dry on top. Every three days find the height of each plant. Measure from the top surface of the sand to the top of each seedling. If you are growing corn plants, gently pull the ends of the leaves above the plant; measure from the sand surface to the highest tip of these leaves. Find the height of each plant in the three cups every three days. Write the heights and the dates in the table. Continue measuring the plants growing in the dark, every 3 days for the next 21 days.

Figure the average (mean) height of plants in each cup each time you measure them. To do this, add together the heights of all the plants in a cup; divide this number by the number of plants in this cup.

Heights of Plants Grown in the Dark for 21 Days

Date Plants Measured	Cup #1	Cup #2	Cup #3
		inches or centimeters	
1. ________ (date seeds planted)	________	________	________
	________	________	________
	________	________	________
	________	________	________
	________	________	________
Average height in each cup:			
2.	________	________	________
	________	________	________
	________	________	________
	________	________	________
	________	________	________
Average height in each cup:			
3.	________	________	________
	________	________	________
	________	________	________
	________	________	________
	________	________	________
Average height in each cup:			
4.	________	________	________
	________	________	________
	________	________	________
	________	________	________
	________	________	________
Average height in each cup:			

5.

________	________	________
________	________	________
________	________	________
________	________	________
________	________	________

Average height in each cup:

6.

________	________	________
________	________	________
________	________	________
________	________	________
________	________	________

Average height in each cup:

7.

________	________	________
________	________	________
________	________	________
________	________	________
________	________	________

Average height in each cup:

8.

________	________	________
________	________	________
________	________	________
________	________	________
________	________	________

Average height in each cup:

Now graph the average height of plants in each cup. Connect the points on the graph that stand for the average height of plants in cup #1; do the same for cups #2 and #3. Use graph on p. 116.

Are the three curves for the three cups of plants exactly alike? Do they have about the same shape? Try to figure out why the seedlings grew slowly when they did; and why they grew fast when they did?

Are plants that are the same age always the same height? Are plants that are the same age and grown in the same cup, the same height? Six seeds were planted in each cup. Did each cup have six seedlings? Did each cup have the same number of plants? What might have happened if you had put only one seed in a cup? What might have happened if you had put only one seed in a cup and you had used only one cup? Do you see why it is good to use several seeds and several cups? Do you see why it is good in experimental work to do the experiment more than once?

4. What parts of a plant grow? Soak 20 seeds of sunflower, tomato, bean, or pea in a glass of water. Place 10 of the soaked seeds on moist paper in a dish (see Adventure 1, Experiment 2 for details of how to do this). Plant the other 10 soaked seeds in a pot of sand (see Adventure 7, Experiment 3 for details). Put the dish and pot of seeds in a warm place but not in direct sunlight or on a radiator.

Make some black marking grease: mix two or three drops of black ink in a piece of butter or oleomargarine the size of a pea seed.

When the seedlings in the dish have roots about one inch long, do this: take a toothpick, dip it in the black grease, and put black marks on three or four of the roots. The marks should be about 1/8 inch (three millimeters) apart. Put one mark on the very tip of each root. Be very careful not to injure the roots when marking them. Now the roots should look like this:

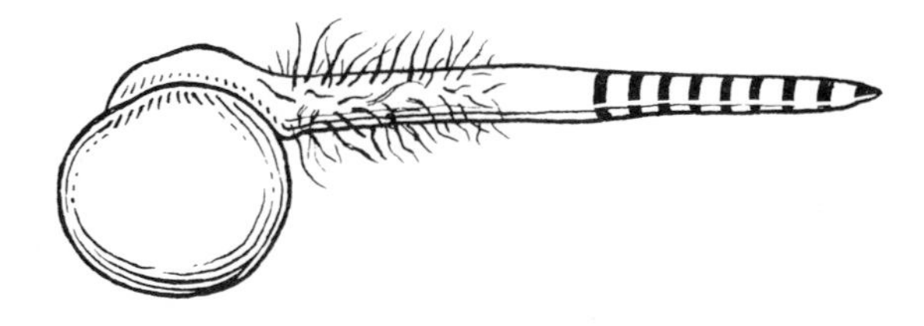

Put the seedlings back in the dish; look at them every few hours during the next day or two days.

When the seedlings in the cup of sand are 1 or 2 inches above the sand surface, do this: with a toothpick and some of the black marking grease, mark the stem and leaves of 3 or 4 seedlings as shown in the diagram. The marks and lines should be 1/8 inch apart. Look at the plants every few hours for several days.

Why does the distance between marks change? Does a root grow most at the very tip? Do the black marks get farthest apart on a stem at the very tip or just below the stem tip? Do certain regions of a root, stem, and leaf grow more than others? Does the whole leaf grow equally? Can you guess where in a root, stem, or leaf the most cells are elongating?

Try this experiment again, but this time cut off the stem and root tips about 1/4 inch behind each tip. Then mark the roots and stems with the black grease. Do the roots and stems grow like they did before?

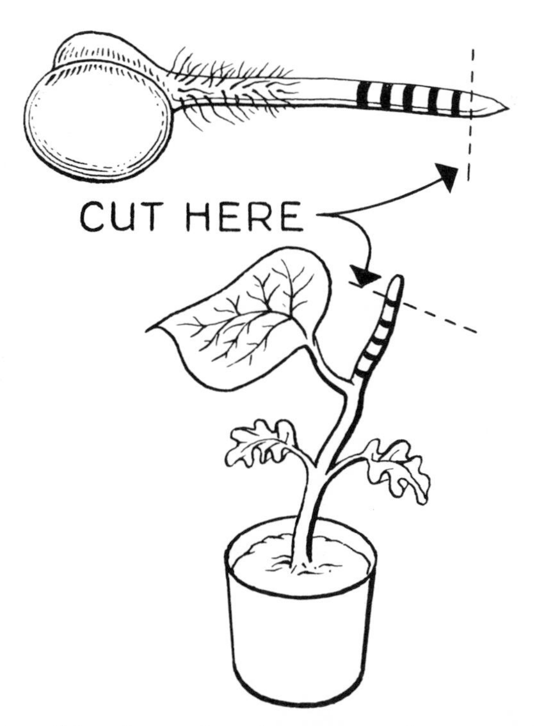

Does this tell you about how stem and root growth are controlled by the stem and root tips?

5. *Can plants "see" light?* Soak 40 oat or corn grains in a glass of water for an hour. Get four waxed paper drinking cups and poke one hole in the bottom of each cup. Cover each hole with a small piece of paper. Nearly fill the cups with clean, wet sand and plant 10 soaked seeds in each cup of sand. The seeds should be spaced equally and about 1/4 inch deep in the sand.

Put the four cups on a tray and place the tray in a dark, warm closet or cabinet. Sprinkle a little water over the sand every day to keep the sand moist. When five or six seedlings in each pot have grown not more than 1/2 inch above the sand, do these things:

Cup 1 Move this cup of seedlings to a warm place in bright light, even in direct sunlight.
Cup 2 Leave this cup in the dark closet.
Cup 3 Use a knife to cut off the top 1/4 inch of half the seedlings. Lay the pot on its side in the dark closet.
Cup 4 Roll a small piece of aluminum foil over the point of a wood pencil so that a small cone is formed.

The cone of aluminum foil should be about 1/2 inch long. Make two of these cones. Put the two cones over the tips of two seedlings. Use a knife to cut off the top 1/8 inch of two other seedlings. Don't do anything to the other seedlings in the cup. Now put this cup of seedlings on a high shelf in a room; the shelf should be across the room from windows or any lights in the room. In other words, the pot of seedlings should get dim light from only one side of the room.

Look at the four pots of seedlings every two hours for the next ten hours. Be careful not to turn or move the cups, though. Also look at them every now and then for a day or two.

Do the plants in cup #1 change color? How long was it until you saw a color change in the seedlings in cup #1? What caused the seedlings to change color? Which seedlings grew taller, those in cup #1 or cup #2?

Did the seedlings in cup #3 all grow straight? What made some seedlings bend? Was it light? Was it heat? What was it? Why did some seedlings not bend in cup #3?

Which way did some seedlings in cup #4 bend, toward the light or away from it? Did all the seedlings bend? Which side of the seedlings must grow faster to make the seedlings bend? Does the side of the plant toward the light or the side away from the light grow faster?

Do you think roots would behave the same way as the shoots did in cups #1, #2, #3 and #4? Figure out an experiment to test your ideas about roots; then try it and see!

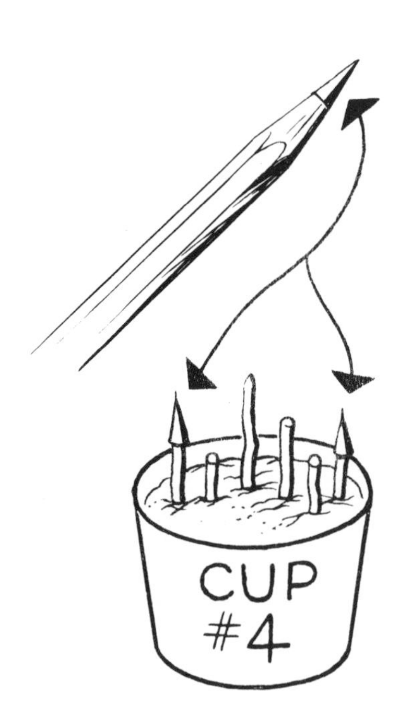

ADVENTURE 8
New Plants From An Old Plant
REPRODUCTION

We're on the *petal* of this flower. You can see the *pistil* with the *stigma* on top. The base of the pistil is the ovary where seeds are being made. Wind is blowing pollen from the six *anthers* over to the stigma.

New Plants From An Old Plant

HEY! Over this way! I've been waiting for you. Yes, I know why it took you so long to get here! I saw you over there on a petal of this flower watching some bees collecting pollen. You should be more careful! Don't forget the reducing pills make you one-millionth your normal size. That bee almost collected you along with the pollen! You would have had an exciting adventure, but I don't think you would like to be stuffed into a bee hive! Or the bee might have eaten you and changed you into beeswax! Wouldn't that have been fun? Well, anyway, you got here safely!

Let's start our adventure up here on a *petal* of this flower. You can tell that we are sitting on a petal because petals of flowers are usually brightly colored. See that big, green "skyscraper" in front of us, the tall thing with the flat top and round bottom? That's the *pistil*. You can see the three parts of the pistil. Look at the flat top of the pistil; that is the *stigma*. The long neck below the stigma is called the *style*. And the round bottom is the *ovary*. Seeds are made in the ovary. We'll go inside the ovary in a few minutes so we can watch seeds being made! You can think of the pistil as the "female" or "womanly" part of this flower. Just as baby kittens are formed inside a mother cat, seeds are formed inside the ovary of the pistil.

Look up there, way above us! A gentle wind is blowing some *pollen* from the *anther* over to the stigma. That pollen was made in one of the anthers. What's an anther? Well, I'll tell you the anther! The pod-like object on the top end of that long stick is an anther. There are six anthers in this flower. The long stick which holds each anther up high in the flower is the *filament*. Can you see the six long filaments? I'll bet you can guess how filaments help pollen to get from the anthers over to the stigma! The anther with its filament is the *stamen*. If you want to, you can think of the stamen as the "male" or "manly" part of the flower. After you see what pollen does, I think you'll know why stamens are the "male" parts of the flower.

Let's slide down this petal to the bottom of the flower. Then we can climb up the side of the pistil to its top, the stigma. We won't have any trouble climbing up the pistil because it is covered with hairs we can hang on to. Do you think you can find your own way to the stigma? Good! See you there! Last one there is a rotten egg!

Quite a view from up here, isn't it? The big balls around us are pollen grains which the wind carried here from the anthers. Look out! The wind moved the pollen grain behind you and it almost stabbed you in the back! The pollen grains in this flower have long, sharp, spikes that stick out in all directions. Those spikes are sharper than any needle made by man! Don't forget you are very reduced in size. If one of the pollen grains rolled over you, a spike would go through you as easily as a knife cuts through cheese! Every kind of flower makes a different kind of pollen grain. Many kinds of flowers don't make pollen grains that have long spikes, but this one does. So be careful! I don't want you to get hurt!

You probably are wondering what this wet, sticky stuff is we are standing in. The stigma is covered with it. Dip your finger in it and taste it; sweet, isn't it? This sweet syrup is made by the stigma cells just underneath the syrup. You can see the cells through the syrup. Well, this syrup does two things. The

There's the *pollen tube* growing toward us from the spiked pollen grain. Let's step inside and see where it's going!

syrup is sticky like a glue; it helps to keep the pollen grains from rolling off the stigma. Also the syrup is food for the pollen grains. Look, over there! The sugar and water in the syrup are going into that pollen grain. Pollen grains aren't green and they can't make their own food by photosynthesis; so they use syrup from the stigma for their food. Watch closely now. You'll see that pollen grain start to grow. Stand back! You don't want to get hit by the *pollen tube* when it pops out of the pollen grain. Here it comes!

The cell inside the pollen grain starts to grow very fast. It gets so large that it pops through the wall of the pollen cell. See that monstrous snake-like cell growing toward us from the pollen grain? It's the *pollen tube*. It sure looks like a long tube, doesn't it? Very soon the tube will start growing down into the stigma. In fact, it will eat part of the stigma for its food as it grows through the stigma. There it goes now! You know that a cell needs water to grow, too. The pollen tube will use water from the cells of the stigma for its water supply. Let's crawl into that pollen tube and find out where it's going! I'll hold these fibers of the pollen tube wall so you can step in. Go ahead! I'll follow you, but hang on to my hand so we don't get lost. Swishhh . . . . . .

I told you this tube was growing fast! As soon as we crawled into this tube cell it carried us down into the pistil. Pretty quickly now the tube will grow into the ovary; then we'll be where seeds are made. Ah, we're entering the ovary now! Can you see the *ovules* inside the ovary?

Ovules are those balls on the end of small stalks. You can see quite a few ovules inside this ovary. Each ovule will grow into a *seed*. But before it can become a seed, the ovule has to be *fertilized*. Watch closely! You'll see it happen! Look behind us inside the pollen tube; see that glob of jelly-like stuff? That's a nucleus; but it's a special nucleus. It is the *sperm nucleus*. Keep your eyes on it because it will do the fertilizing. It won't be long now! The pollen tube we're in is starting to grow into an ovule. Here we go! Be ready to duck your head! You don't want the sperm nucleus to bump you as it goes into the ovule. Watch out! Here it comes! No one knows how the sperm nucleus does this, but it will find a partner nucleus inside the ovule. Wow! Did you see it find its partner? The sperm nucleus just joined with a special nucleus in the ovule—the *egg nucleus*. Now you have seen an egg being fertilized! When a sperm nucleus and egg nucleus come together, that is fertilization.

Now watch that fertilized egg. You will see it start to divide and grow; it will grow into an *embryo plant!* You have seen embryo plants many times. Oh, you don't think you have? Well, each tiny plant inside a seed is an embryo plant. I know you've seen those before! When you eat a peanut or bean you are eating embryo plants. In fact, you eat the whole ovule or seed with the embryo inside! The skin of the peanut or bean is the outside of the ovule. The skin is called the *seed coat*. The seed coat covers the embryo plant which grew from the fertilized egg.

Well; you've seen another of the great marvels of nature. You have watched *reproduction!* As we sit here in the ovule watching the fertilized egg grow and become an embryo plant, let's think about some of the things we saw and did.

First, we saw pollen blow in the wind from the anther over to the stigma. Then the pollen grain started growing and a pollen tube grew out of the grain. We climbed into the pollen tube and we hitched a ride inside the tube as it grew very long. We were inside the tube as it grew down through the stigma, style, and into the ovary! Then the tube went into an ovule. We saw a sperm nucleus from inside the pollen tube go into the ovule and find an egg nucleus. It almost hit us as it floated by!

Now we're down in the ovary and can see the *ovules*. We can even watch the sperm nucleus fertilizing the egg!

We even watched the sperm nucleus join with the egg nucleus; we saw fertilization! Now we are watching the fertilized egg divide, grow, and become an embryo plant.

This process of one plant forming seeds which grow into new plants is called reproduction. There are an awful lot of things about reproduction that botanists haven't found out! You can think of some of these things, too. Did you wonder why the pollen tube grew down into the stigma instead of up into the air? Did you wonder how the pollen tube found the ovule? Why did the sperm nucleus join with the egg nucleus? Why didn't it join with some other nucleus? Did you wonder why the egg grew only after it was fertilized? Why didn't the egg grow into an embryo plant without being fertilized? And once the fertilized egg started growing into an embryo plant, why didn't it keep right on growing into a very large plant? I wish I knew the answers to these and dozens of other questions about reproduction. I guess the answers will have to be secrets until some botanists do the right experiments to find the answers!

Golly; time really has gone fast! We lost all track of time watching this flower in action. The effect of the reducing pills will wear off in a few moments. Let's just let ourselves explode out of this seed and ovary as we return to normal size! Be careful of your head as we start to get larger! You may crack your skull on the seed coats as you burst out of the seed! Here we go! See you on the next adventure when we explore the nucle . . . ussss . . ss.

Things to Do and Think About

1. Parts of flowers. Get some fresh flowers of sweet pea, petunia, lily, bean, tomato, tobacco, cotton, hibiscus, morning glory, apple, orange, or other "simple" flowers. If you explain to a florist why you need some flowers, he will probably be glad to give you some he is about to throw away. See if you can find the main parts of the flower:

sepals (green and leaf-like, around the underside of the flower)

petals	filament	style
stamens	pistil	ovary
anther	stigma	

Count the number of sepals, petals, and stamens in a flower. Are they multiples of the same number?

Can you find pollen in the anthers? Is the tip of the stigma wet and sticky? Touch the stigma with your tongue; does it taste sweet?

With a knife, carefully cut the flower in half from top to bottom; make the cut so it splits the pistil in half from top to bottom. Can you see where the plumbing pipes in the stem below the flower go into the sepals, petals, stamens, and pistil? Can you see the ovules inside the ovary? How many ovules are there? Can you see the stalk that joins each ovule to the ovary wall? This little stalk is the *funiculus*.

Cut an anther crosswise. Can you see the chambers in which the pollen is formed?

Try drawing a picture of a flower to show all the parts. Label each part with its name.

2. Parts of fruits. Get two of each of the following fruits:

bean or pea pod	orange or grapefruit
tomato	apple

Look at each fruit very carefully. Which end of the fruit was connected to the plant? Can you find any parts of the flower at the end of the fruit that was connected to the plant? Are any parts of the flower at the other end of the fruit?

With a knife, cut each fruit in half lengthwise. Can you find the ovules (now growing into seeds)? Can you see the little stalk (funiculus) that joins each ovule to the fruit wall? How many ovules are there? Which parts of these fruits do you eat? Which parts of these fruits are soft and fleshy? Which parts are hardened? Are the ovules surrounded by juice or air?

Now take a whole fruit of each kind; cut each fruit cross-wise. Is the inside of the fruit divided into sections? Is the part of the fruit that you eat divided into sections?

Are the ovules joined to each section of the fruit? Are the ovules joined to each section of the fruit at any special place, or do they join any place along the wall of each section?

Compare the cut fruits of each kind, one cut lengthwise and the other cut cross-wise. Can you see that the ovules are formed in rows? Compare the number of rows of ovules with the number of sections in each fruit. For example, in bean and pea pods, do you see the two rows of ovules and one section?

When you eat string beans, are you really eating a vegetable? When you eat tomatoes, are you eating a vegetable?

Look carefully at the inside of an orange or grapefruit. The juice is in long sacs that are like fat, juicy, hairs.

After you eat an apple you throw the "core" away. What plant parts are in the apple core?

You may eat your experimental material now!

3. Parts of seeds. Get one or two fresh, green, string beans or fresh pea pods. Open the fruit (called a "pod") by cutting it from end to end. Do you see the small stalk that joins each seed to the pod? The stalk is called the *funiculus*. The funiculus attaches to a swollen edge of the ovary wall; this edge of the ovary wall is the *placenta*.

Snap off a seed. Did it break where the funiculus joins the seed? The scar left on the seed where the funiculus breaks off is called the *hilum*. Carefully peel the seed coats away from a seed. How thick are the seed coats? Let the seed coats dry; are they made of very hard cells?

After the seed coats are removed from a pea or bean seed, the embryo is left. Carefully pull the two halves of the embryo apart. These two large halves are the *cotyledons* or seed leaves. What is the small thing lying between the cotyledons? Is it joined to each cotyledon? Which end of this object would grow into the stem and leaves of the plant? What part of a plant would the other end become?

Get a fresh corn grain (really a fruit) or soak some dry corn grains in water for a couple of hours. With a knife, carefully cut the corn grain in half like this:

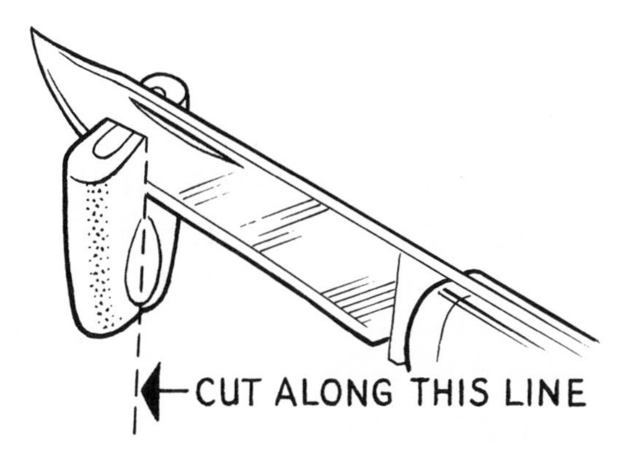

Use a magnifying glass and look at the cut surface of the corn grain. Does it look like the inside of a pea or bean seed? Can you see the outer, hard, yellowish layer? That is the fruit wall (ovary wall). The wall of the corn seed is the layer just inside the yellowish layer. Can you see the white stuff that fills most of the inside of the seed? It is stored food. Can you find the yellow embryo along one side of the corn grain? If you have a strong magnifying glass, look at the embryo. You will be able to see three parts: one cotyledon; a part that will grow into the stem and leaves; a part that will grow and become the roots.

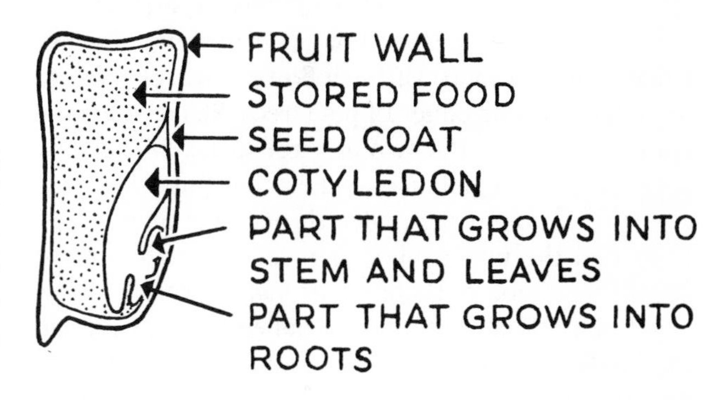

4. What kinds of food are in seeds? Get a small bottle of tincture of iodine; the kind found in drugstores and medicine cabinets. Also get several different kinds of seeds and grains – bean, pea, corn, peanut, weed, pine, oat, etc. If they are dry, soak them in water for one or two hours. Then test each seed:

Test A. Cut a seed in half and put a drop of tincture of iodine on the cut surface. Wait a few seconds and look at the color.

Test B. Cut a seed in half and rub the cut surface over a piece of writing paper. Rub the seed back and forth over the same place on the paper. Does the paper look "greasy" where you rubbed the seed?

Also do test "A" on some flour or the cut surface of a potato. Also rub butter or oleomargarine on some paper. What happens in each test? Do these tests tell you the kind of stored food in each kind of seed? What use is stored food to the embryo?

When you eat corn, peas, or beans, are you eating a vegetable, a fruit, or a seed?

5. A seed collection. Make a collection of all the kinds of seeds you can find. Don't forget to include a seed in your collection that is about six inches long, hairy, and shaped like a football; you'll find it in the grocery store!

Compare the seeds for size, color, hardness, and kind of stored food inside them. Also look for differences in shape, color and size of seeds from the same kind of plant (see Adventure 9 for some reasons for these differences).

Look for special things the seeds have that help them get carried from one place to another. For example, the "parachute" of dandelion seeds helps them to be carried by the wind.

Some very attractive and fascinating displays can be made with seed collections. They make beautiful charts for the wall; put real seeds on the chart with glue, or put them in small bottles or transparent bags.

6. *You can grow pollen tubes.* You will need a microscope, slides, and cover slips for this experiment.

Dissolve a tablespoon of sugar in a cup of water. Collect several kinds of fresh flowers, tassels of corn, or pollen-forming cones of pine trees. Shake some pollen on to a slide. Put two or three drops of the sugar solution over the pollen or anther; then put a cover slip over this. Look at the pollen through the microscope. First find the pollen under low power of the microscope; then look at them under high power.

Look at different kinds of pollen grains. Compare the kinds you look at for size and shape. Try making drawings of the kinds of pollen grains you look at.

Put several kinds of pollen in sugar solutions on slides; put one kind of pollen on each slide. Cover the sugar and pollen on each slide with a cover slip. Put several layers of paper towels or newspapers in the bottom of a pie pan; wet the paper with water and pour off the extra water. Then lay the slides of pollen on top of the moist paper and cover the pie pan with a large plate.
Put the set-up in a warm place, but not in sunlight or on a radiator. Look at the pollen on each slide every few hours for two days. Use a microscope to look at the pollen. Usually, but not always, some of the pollen will start to grow and form pollen tubes. If you don't have any luck the first time, try again. You will find it worth the effort to see the living, growing, pollen tubes!

7. *What ways are flowers of different plants alike and unlike?* Collect several different kinds of fresh flowers. Include flowers of sunflower or dandelion, rose, and grass in your collection. Look carefully at each fresh flower. Observe the likenesses and differences of several flowers. Look for the following:

A. Number of sepals, petals, stamens, and pistils.
B. Shape and color of sepals, petals, stamens, and pistils.
C. Are all the petals the same shape and size in a flower? Do the petals in some flowers join together and form a tube or funnel?
D. Are some flowers really groups of flowers? For example, look at a sunflower or dandelion.
E. Are the filaments in a flower all the same length? Are some filaments long and others short? Do some filaments join together?
F. Does a grass flower have sepals and petals?
G. Do all pistils have a style?
H. How many different shapes of stigmas can you find?
I. Is the ovary always above the place where the sepals, petals, and stamens join the stem?
J. Do the sepals, petals, and stamens ever join on to the side of the pistil?
K. How many seeds or ovules are inside the ovary of each flower? If you can't get fresh flowers for this experiment, use the colored pictures of flowers in encyclopedias, books on flowers, etc. Or look at the flowers in the windows of a flower shop.

8. *Other ways of reproducing plants.* Visit a nursery or home garden supply store and see what ways of reproducing plants are used there. Look in the library for books on home gardening and how to raise house plants. Find out all you can about grafting, slip cutting, leaf cutting, budding, etc. Then try doing these things yourself with plants in and around your home. You'll be surprised how easy and fun it is!

Write the Agricultural Extension Service, at the College of Agriculture in your state; ask them for free bulletins on how to propagate garden and house plants. Most State Colleges of Agriculture have these bulletins; they will be glad to send you copies. Be sure to give them your name and address so they'll know where to send them!

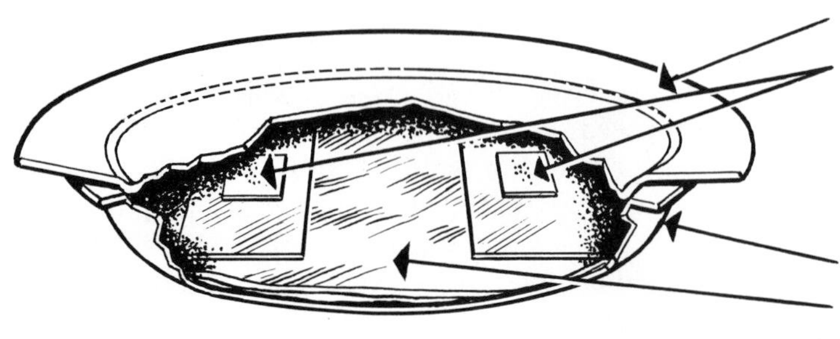

ADVENTURE 9

As 'Equal' As Two Peas In A Pod

HEREDITY

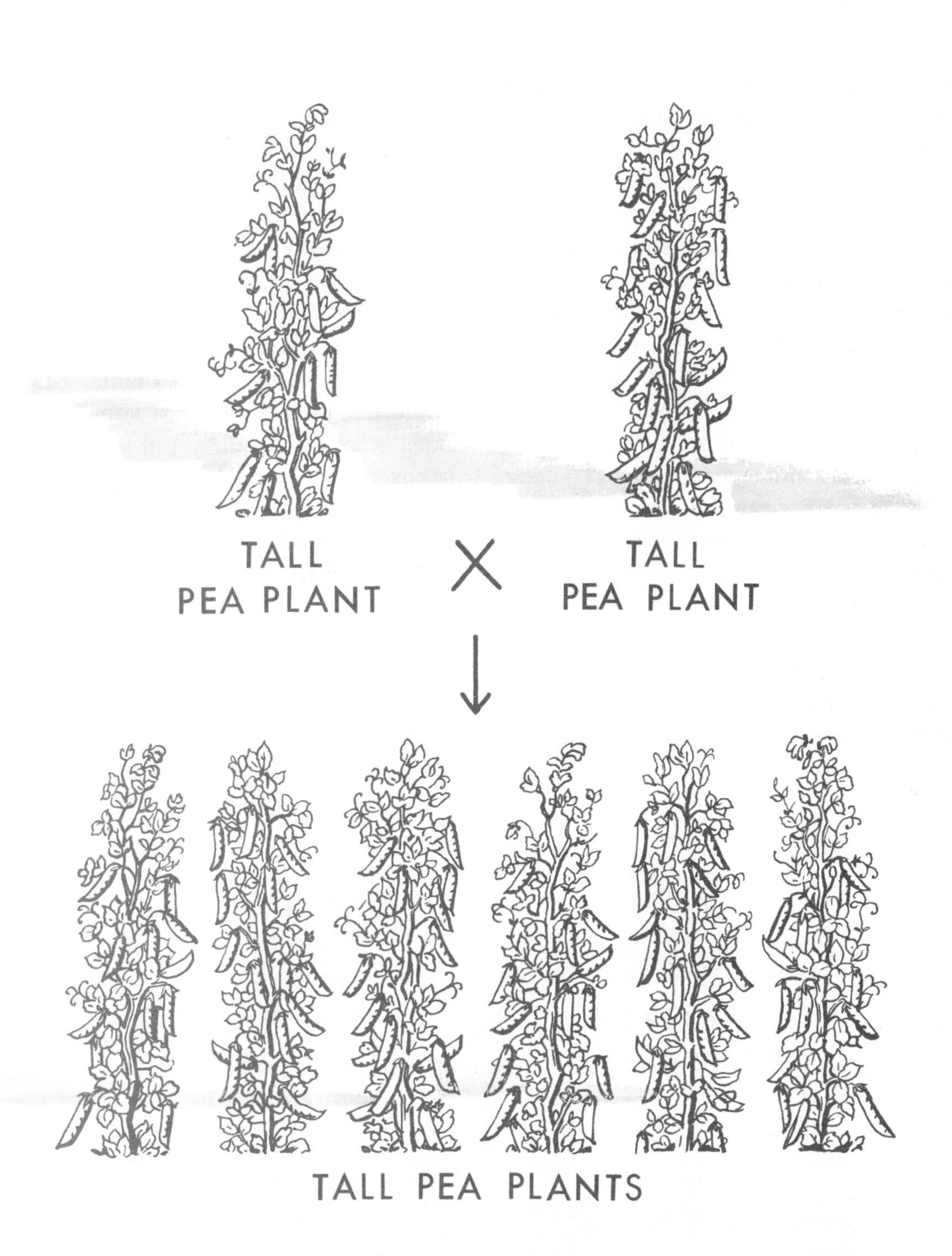

Do you like puzzles? I have already guessed that you do. I'd like to tell you about a puzzle that a man named Gregor Mendel tried to solve 100 years ago. But I won't tell you the answer to the puzzle—not yet, anyway! First let's see if you can solve it. Gregor Mendel became famous for *his* solution. Others had tried to find an answer for hundreds and thousands of years, too, but Mendel solved it first. Let's see what puzzled Mendel and how he solved it. Let's see if you can solve the puzzle, too! I'll bet you can!

We all know that pea plants make pea seeds. And what do pea seeds grow into? This is too easy! Of course; pea seeds grow into pea plants. But this simple answer covers up a very hard puzzle: What inside the pea seed tells it to grow into a plant which looks like a pea plant? Have you ever wondered about that? Gregor Mendel wondered about it for several years. He wondered about something else, too. He noticed that some pea plants are tall; and seeds from these tall plants always grow into more tall plants. This puzzled Mendel quite a bit. He finally decided the tall plants are *pure-breeding* tall plants. And he thought about another problem. He noticed that some pea plants are short; and seeds from these short plants always grow into more short plants. Again, he decided the short plants are *pure-breeding* short plants. But why are some pea plants tall and some short? How does a pure-breeding tall pea plant tell its seeds to grow into tall plants? How does a pure-breeding short pea plant tell its seeds to grow into short plants?

Now, Mendel knew how a seed is formed in a flower. He realized that a pollen grain sends a pollen tube into the ovary of the flower. He also knew that a sperm nucleus from inside the pollen tube fertilizes the egg nucleus inside the ovule. So Mendel thought:

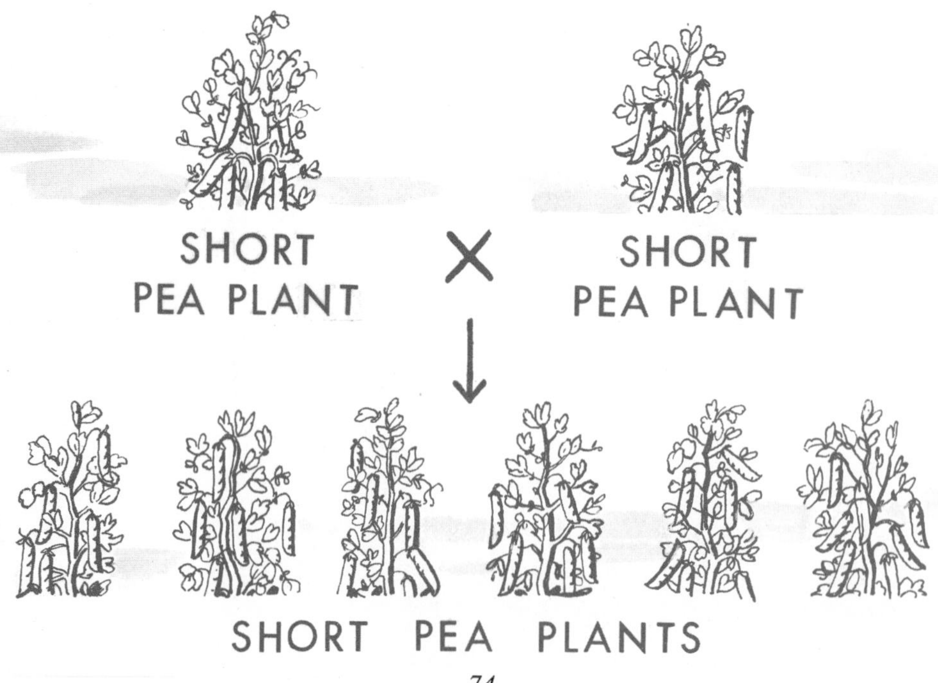

"I'll take the pollen grains from a short pea plant and put them in the flower on a tall plant. The sperm nucleus from a short plant will fertilize the egg from a tall plant. What will happen then? Will I get seeds that grow into tall plants? Or will they grow into short plants? Or will they grow into middle-sized plants?" This was Mendel's first experiment.

Mendel grew several pure-breeding tall plants and pure-breeding short plants. He carefully pulled the anthers out of the flowers on the tall plants. Only the pistil was left in these flowers. Then he rubbed the anthers in the flowers on the short plants with a toothpick. Some yellow-colored pollen grains stuck to the toothpick. He rubbed these pollen grains on the stigma of the pistil in each flower on the tall plants. Then Mendel waited for the seeds to grow and develop.

Finally the seeds were ripe and Mendel planted them. Was he surprised! All the seeds grew into tall plants! He couldn't find any short plants. And there weren't any middle-sized plants, either! Even though the pollen was from a short plant, all the seeds grew into tall plants. This really puzzled Mendel. Does it puzzle you? He decided to do a second experiment!

Mendel waited until the new tall plants from the first experiment produced flowers. Then he let each flower on these tall plants form its own seeds. Again he waited until the seeds were ripe. Then he collected the seeds and planted them. The 1064 seeds he planted did some curious things! Some seeds grew into tall plants; others grew into short plants! There were 787 tall plants, and 277 seeds grew into short plants!

Mendel was really puzzled now! How could seeds which grow into short plants be formed from pollen and ovules made by tall plants? Mendel didn't give up! The puzzling results of his experiments only made him want to find the answer all the more!

For his third experiment Mendel waited again until the seeds from the second experiment formed flowers. Then he let each flower on the tall and short plants form its own seeds. So the sperm from pollen grains in a flower on a short plant fertilized eggs in the same flower. And the sperm from pollen grains in a flower on a tall plant fertilized eggs in the same flower. What kinds of seeds do you think were formed this time? Did these seeds grow into tall or short plants?

When Mendel saw the plants which grew from the seeds formed in his third experiment, he was sure something had gone wrong! But after thinking about his experiments, he figured out how it all happened! Can you figure it out, too? Let's see how Mendel solved the puzzle, as he thought about his tall and short plants.

First Mendel thought about the pure-breeding tall plants. He said to himself, "I'll let *T* stand for the pollen sperm formed by a tall plant. I'll also let *T* stand for the egg nucleus formed by a flower on a tall plant. Now, when the sperm *T* fertilizes the egg *T*, what will result? The new seed will have to be *TT*. The *TT* will tell this seed to grow into a tall plant."

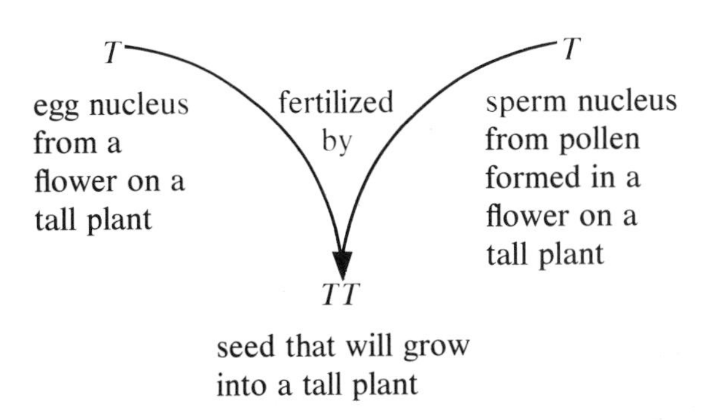

Now Mendel thought about the seeds that were pure-breeding for short plants. Mendel decided to let *t* stand for the sperm from pollen formed by a flower on a short plant. He also let *t* stand for the egg formed in a flower on a short plant. Then he thought,

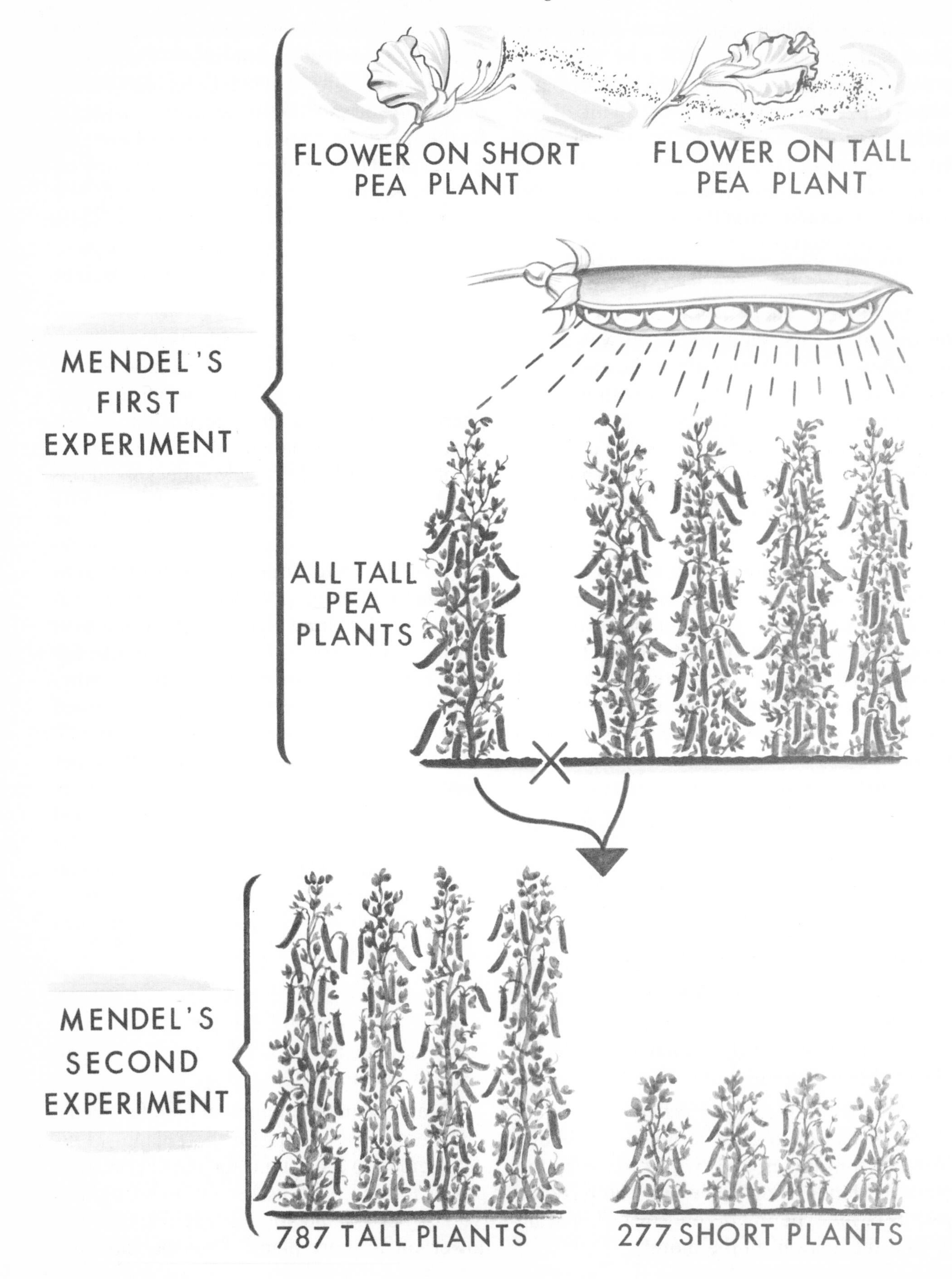
FLOWER ON SHORT PEA PLANT
FLOWER ON TALL PEA PLANT
MENDEL'S FIRST EXPERIMENT
ALL TALL PEA PLANTS
MENDEL'S SECOND EXPERIMENT
787 TALL PLANTS
277 SHORT PLANTS

"When the sperm *t* fertilizes an egg *t*, what kind of seed will be formed? The new seed will have to be *tt*. And a seed that is *tt* will have to grow into a short plant! There isn't a large *T* inside each cell of the seed to tell it to grow into a tall plant! And a seed that is *tt* will become a pure-breeding short plant." And this is exactly what the seeds were. Each grew into a short plant that was pure breeding!

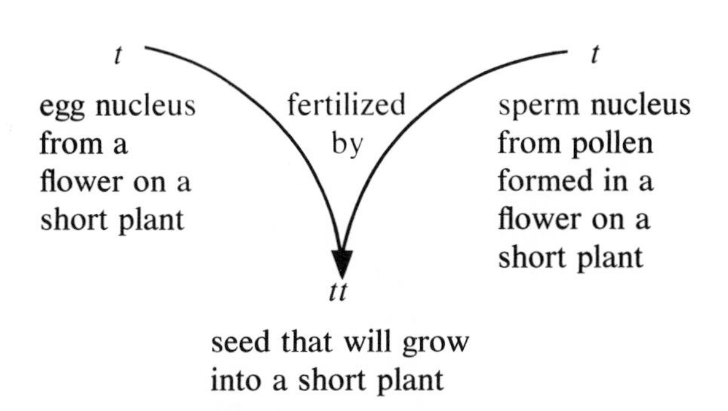

Next Mendel figured out what happened in his first experiment. Remember, he used pollen from a flower on a short plant to fertilize eggs in flowers on pure-breeding tall plants. Mendel knew that if the short plant is *tt* and breeds pure, the pollen from a short plant must be *t*. He knew the tall plant is *TT* and breeds pure, so its eggs must all be *T*. Now, when the sperm nucleus *t* fertilizes the egg *T*, what will result? The fertilized egg must be *Tt!* Mendel looked at his notes; the seed formed from this fertilized egg *(Tt)* grew into a tall plant. The plant was not short or halfway between a tall plant and a short plant; it was a tall plant. How could this be?

Here is where Mendel showed his genius! He got the idea that because *Tt* grows into a tall plant, *T* must dominate over *t!* He decided that when a seed is *Tt* and has a mixture of *T* and *t* in it, the seed does only what *T* tells it to do! *T* is *dominant* and is the ruler! Mendel called *t recessive*. This means *t* can only tell the seed what to do when there aren't any dominating *T*'s around! A seed must be pure *tt* to grow into a short plant! So now we see there are two kinds of tall plants: *TT* and *Tt*. There is only one kind of short plant: *tt*. By the way, Mendel called the *Tt* kind of tall plant, a *hybrid* tall plant.

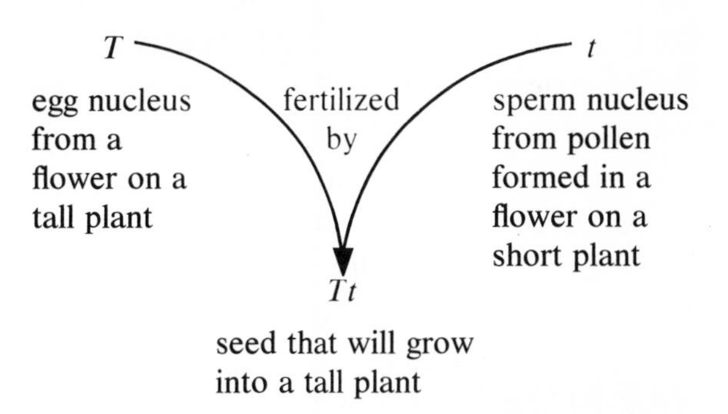

So far, so good! I'd say Mendel did some sharp thinking, wouldn't you?

How did Mendel solve the next problem? In his second experiment, Mendel used pollen grains from a hybrid tall plant *(Tt)* to fertilize eggs on the same plant. Do you remember that three-fourths of the 1064 seeds planted by Mendel grew into tall plants? One-fourth of the 1064 seeds grew into short plants. After thinking about this, Mendel figured it this way. The parent plant was a hybrid tall plant. It was *Tt*. When it formed pollen grains, the pollen grains were either *T* or *t*. Half the pollen grains were *T;* the other half were *t*. Can you see what kinds of eggs were formed by the hybrid tall plant? Mendel decided that half the eggs were *T* and the other half were *t*. Do you see why? Do you see what happened when the two kinds of eggs *T* and *t* were fertilized by the two kinds of sperm from the pollen *T* and *t*?

Eggs of a hybrid tall plant *Tt* will be either *T* or *t*. Sperms from pollen made by a hybrid tall plant *Tt* will be either *T* or *t*. You can see that these four things happened:

T egg fertilized by *T* sperm ➧ *TT* seed
T egg fertilized by *t* sperm ➧ *Tt* seed
t egg fertilized by *T* sperm ➧ *Tt* seed
t egg fertilized by *t* sperm ➧ *tt* seed

Of course, one egg is fertilized by only one sperm; we will get all these things happening only if we have many eggs to be fertilized, and many sperm to do the fertilizing.

If you look closely at what happened, you will see that three kinds of seeds were formed; *TT*, *Tt*, and *tt*. Usually, out of 4 seeds, one should be *TT*, two should be *Tt*, and one should be *tt*. How many of these four seeds will grow into tall plants? That's right; three seeds! *TT*, *Tt*, and *Tt*. And what will the fourth plant be like? You're right again! It is *tt* and it will be a short plant. There should be three tall plants to one short plant. Now, do these ideas agree with what Mendel found in his second experiment? Mendel found that 787 seeds grew into tall plants; 277 seeds grew into short plants. And 787 is about three times larger than 277! That is almost exactly what we expected! Three tall plants to one short plant!

Again, so far, so good!

Would you expect the 277 short plants formed in the second experiment to be pure-breeding? If the pollen from a flower on one of these short plants is used to fertilize eggs in flowers on the same plant, do you think the seeds will grow into tall or short plants? Yes; you should expect the short plants to be pure-breeding for shortness. And they did! That is exactly what Mendel found; the seeds formed by these short plants did grow into short plants!

What about the 787 seeds that grew into tall plants? Did they all breed true for tallness? Do you think that flowers on these plants should all form seeds that grow into tall plants? You're right! Only some of the plants should breed true. About one-third of the plants *were* pure-breeding. The seeds that grew into these tall plants must have been *TT*. Can you see why? And about two-thirds of the 787 tall plants *were not* pure-breeding for tallness. These tall plants formed seeds that grew into both tall and short plants; they were the *Tt* kind.

It was simple experiments with pea plants like these that Mendel did. Yet, it is for these experiments we call Mendel the Father of the Science of Heredity. Other scientists have found that the same rules of dominance and recessiveness apply to all organisms—even you!

Now that you know this, you can begin to see why you look somewhat like your parents. You have inherited characters from them! They gave you your eye color, your hair color, your height, your skin color, and all the other things that make you a particular human being. When you were formed, the egg in your mother and sperm from your father had all of these characters in them. Some of the characters in the sperm and egg were dominant; some were recessive. When the egg got fertilized by the sperm, the dominant and recessive characters came together. And you are the result! If you got a dominant character from either parent, then you show this character. If you got a recessive character from both parents, then you show the recessive form of that character.

Let's take an example. Some people have bent little fingers and others have straight little fingers. Bent little finger is dominant, and straight little finger is recessive. Look at your little fingers; are your little fingers bent or straight?

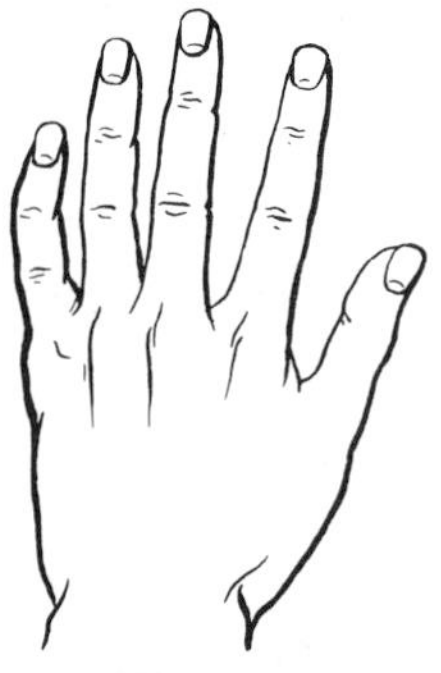

BENT LITTLE FINGER (DOMINANT)

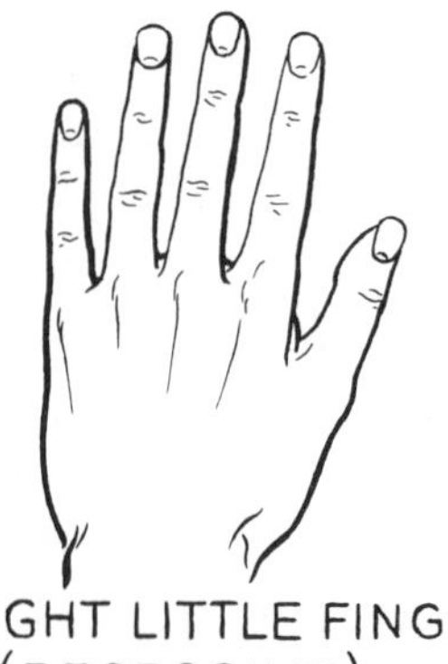

STRAIGHT LITTLE FINGER (RECESSIVE)

If your little fingers are bent, your cells have inherited from your parents at least one dominant character for bent little fingers. You may be pure breeding for bent little fingers, or you may be a hybrid! When your little fingers started to grow, the character for bent little fingers in the cells of your little fingers told them not to grow straight. So now you have bent little fingers! If your little fingers are straight, you know you are pure-breeding for this recessive character. Both your parents have passed on to you the recessive character for straight fingers.

You are probably wondering where all these dominant and recessive characters are in an egg or sperm nucleus. You have asked a good question and a very important one! Do you remember that when we took a trip through a cell, we saw the nucleus? Do you remember seeing the long stringy chromosomes inside the nucleus? Well, it's the chromosomes that contain all the characters that tell the cell what to do!

In each of your cells there is a nucleus. And each nucleus has in it chromosomes. In fact, each nucleus of your cells has 46 chromosomes in it. These 46 chromosomes contain all the characters needed to tell your cells how to make you! Amazing, isn't it! Your chromosomes are like a library of books. Each character is a book with all the directions and recipes needed to make part of you! All these directions are coded in the chemical that your chromosomes are made of. Have you heard of this chemical? It is deoxyribonucleic acid! That's too big a tongue-twister even for scientists, so they call it DNA, for short.

It isn't known how the directions are coded in your DNA, but scientists are busy trying to find out. We do know each recipe for a part of you—such as eye color, hair color, how to make a nose or toe—is in a *gene*. Each gene in your cells is made of DNA. Of course, each of your genes is made of a slightly different kind of DNA. The DNA of each gene has all the directions needed to tell your cells how to do one thing; so each gene must be a different kind of DNA. But you are made of thousands of different things, and your cells do thousands of different jobs. This means that each of your cells has thousands of genes! Since each gene in the cell is a different kind of DNA, there are thousands of kinds of DNA. There are probably 10,000 to 100,000 different genes in each cell of your body! Don't brag about it, though! Even the simplest plants and animals have thousands of different genes in their cells!

Next time you take some reducing pills and go into a cell, take a close look at the chromosomes and genes. You may even be able to see the molecule of DNA in each gene! Even when you see the gene and its DNA, it won't be easy for you to believe those tiny bits of DNA contain all the directions for making a living cell! Living things are truly marvelous!

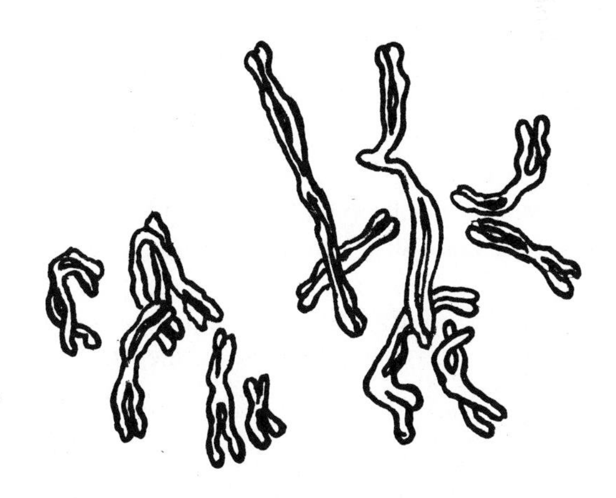

Each bean plant cell has 12 pairs of chromosomes.

Things to Do and Think About

1. Taking a close look at yourself. Here are 5 inherited characters of human beings. Read about them; then look at yourself. See what you can learn about yourself!

A. **Sex.** If the 45th and 46th chromosomes in every nucleus of a person have the *same* shape, then the human being is a girl. Let's have "X" stand for the 45th chromosome. Since the 46th chromosome has the same shape as the 45th chromosome, #46 must also be "X." Then we can let "XX" stand for a girl! If the 45th and 46th chromosomes in each nucleus of a person have *different* shapes, then the human being is a boy. Let's let "X" stand for the 45th chromosome. Since #46 is different from #45, we can let "Y" stand for the 46th chromosome. Then "XY" stands for a boy! X and Y chromosomes are called the *sex chromosomes*. They tell your body to become a boy or girl. What are you, XX or XY?

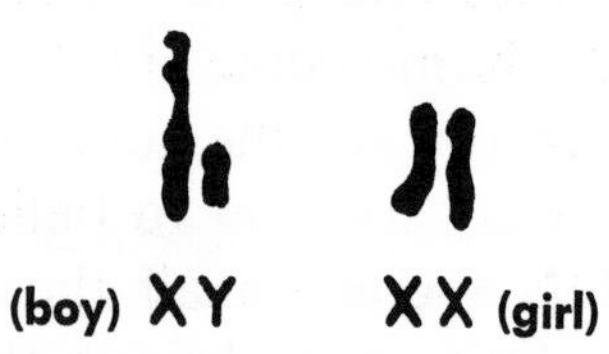

All fathers are XY because they are male (men). All mothers are XX because they are female (women). A father can pass on to each child either an X or a Y chromosome in the sperm. Because a mother is "XX," she can pass on to each child only an X chromosome in the egg. It is luck which chromosome (X or Y) happens to be in the sperm that fertilizes the egg.

Will the baby be a boy or girl if the father gives the child an X chromosome and the mother gives an X chromosome? Will the baby be a boy or girl if the father gives a Y chromosome and the mother gives an X chromosome? Does the sex chromosome in the sperm (from the father) or in the egg (from the mother) tell the baby to be a boy or a girl?

B. **Eye Color.** The color of your eyes is controlled by a gene in the nucleus of every cell in your eyes. Of course, the other cells in your body have this gene too. If one or both of your parents gave you a dominant gene for eye color, your eyes are brown or some dark color. If *both* parents gave you a recessive gene for eye color, your eyes are blue, grey, or some light color.

Let *E* be the dominant gene for brown or dark eyes. Let *e* be the recessive gene for blue or light-colored eyes. Do your cells have a dominant gene (*E*) or are you pure recessive (*ee*)?

C. **Ear Lobes.** Look at your ear lobes. If your ear lobes look something like this at least one of

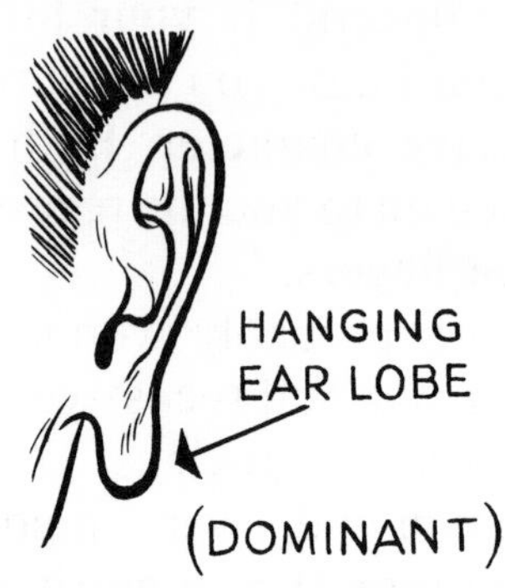

your parents gave you a dominant gene for hanging ear lobes. This dominant gene, *L*, which is in each nucleus of your body, has told your ear lobes to grow that way.

If your ear lobes look something like this

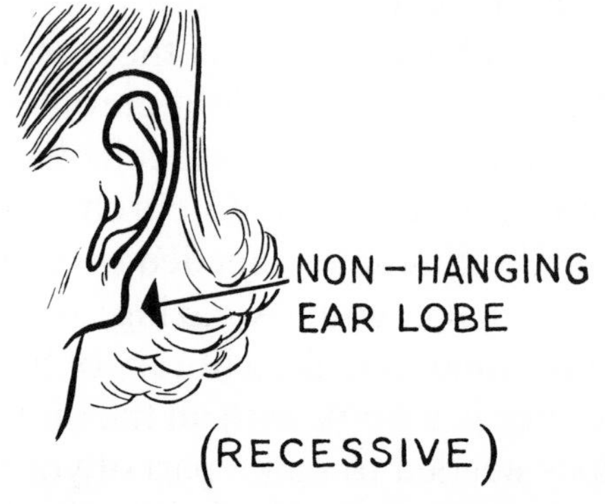

both of your parents gave you a recessive gene for non-hanging ear lobes. We'll call this gene *l*. If your ear lobes are non-hanging, your cells are pure recessive, *ll*.

D. **Bent Little Fingers.** We found in the adventure that bent little fingers is a dominant character. Are your little fingers bent? If they are, each cell in your body has at least one dominant gene for bent little fingers. Let's call this gene *P*. One or both of your parents passed on to you a gene that is *P*.

If your little fingers are straight, then you show the pure recessive character. You are pure-breeding for straight little fingers; *both* of your parents passed on to you a recessive gene for straight little fingers. Your cells are all *pp*.

E. **Mid-digital Hair.** Do you have hair on your fingers between the first and second joints? If you do, you have mid-digital hair! Even a few short hairs or fuzz count as mid-digital hair. If you have mid-digital hair, your cells all have at least one dominant gene for this character. Let's call it *M*. Either the sperm or egg from which you were formed, or perhaps both, contained an *M* gene. If you don't have mid-digital hair, you are pure-breeding for this recessive character. *Both* the sperm and the egg which formed you contained the recessive gene, *m*. Your cells are all *mm*.

Now you know about five inherited characters of human beings! You also know whether you have the dominant or recessive form of each character. Now take a close look at your parents. If you show a dominant character, find out which parent gave you the dominant gene. If both parents also have the dominant character, does this mean that you are pure-breeding for the dominant character? The answer is—maybe yes; maybe no! You may or may not be pure-breeding for the dominant character. Can you figure out why you can't be sure?

Also find out what characters your sisters or brothers inherited, if you have any. If any grandparents, uncles, aunts, or other close relatives live near you, find if they show the dominant or recessive characters. You can build up a family tree for each character. You may be able to discover from this family tree if your cells are pure dominant or hybrid for each character!

2. Some magic tricks with your friends. Would you like to try a magic trick on your friends? If a friend of yours does not know about human heredity, then you can play a neat trick on him! While you say several magical words and wave your arms around as if you are getting some help from a "spirit," look at your friend's eyes, ear lobes, and little fingers. If your friend has dark-colored eyes, tell him the spirit has told you one of his parents has dark eyes. If your friend's ear lobes hang down, then you can tell him the spirit has just told you one of his parents has ear lobes that hang down. And if his little fingers are bent, you can tell him one of his parents has bent little fingers. Sometimes both parents will have the same characters that your friend has, but you cannot "mind read" that. Be very mystical when you tell your friend what his parents are like; don't let him know you had to look at his eye color, ear lobes, or little fingers to perform your magic. You will really mystify your friends with your "superhuman" powers!

A few words of caution! On the average, one out of eight of your friends will not have any of the three dominant characters; he will have light-colored eyes, ear lobes that don't hang down, and straight little fingers. When you try your magic on him, the "spirit" cannot tell you anything about his parents. His parents may or may not have dark eyes, bent little fingers, or hanging ear lobes. You will have to tell your friend that the "spirit" refuses to tell you anything about his parents!

3. Albino and green corn plants. Here is a picture of normal green corn plants and albino (white) corn

Unlike the green corn, the white plants pictured here lack a dominant gene and cannot make chlorophyll.

plants. The green corn plants have at least one dominant gene (*G*) in each of their cells; the dominant gene tells them to make chlorophyll. The albino plants do not have this dominant gene in their cells. Instead, they have two recessive (*gg*) genes in their cells. The albino plant cannot make chlorophyll.

Would you expect albino plants to live very long? If you could get the albino plants to live and produce flowers (tassels and ears), would they breed pure for the albino color?

All the plants in this picture grew from grains formed on one ear of corn. When all the grains from this ear were planted, 450 green seedlings and 145 albino seedlings grew up. Divide 450 by 145. Is the answer closest to 1, 2, 3, or 4?

The pollen used to make the 595 corn grains came from a plant that was G*g*. It was a hybrid plant. Was this plant green or albino in color?

The eggs used to make the 595 corn grains were on the same ear of corn; this ear grew on a plant that was G*g*. It was a hybrid plant. Was this a green or an albino plant?

Try to figure out which gene, *G* or *g*, was in each pollen grain. Out of 595 pollen grains, about how many of them were *G*? About how many were *g*?

Try to figure out which gene, *G* or *g*, was in each egg. Out of 595 eggs, about how many were *G*? About how many were *g*?

When the sperms from the pollen grains fertilized the eggs, what kinds of seeds were formed? Were they *GG*, *Gg*, or *gg*? How many of each kind were there in the 595 grains that grew into 450 green seedlings and 145 albino seedlings?

4. Inheritance of color of corn grains. Take a look at this ear of corn. The dark-colored grains are purple;

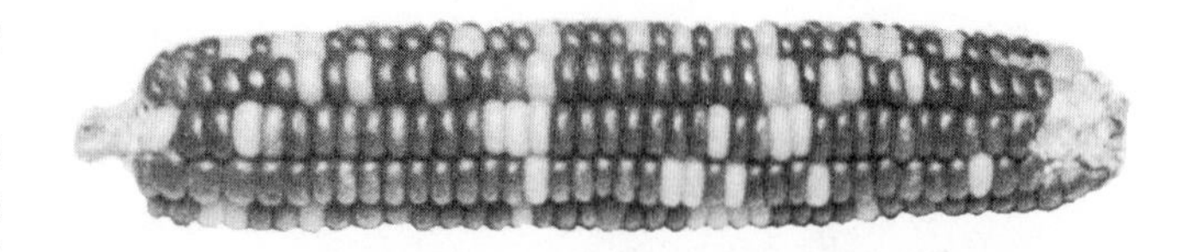

the light-colored grains are yellow. Purple color (*P*) is dominant; yellow color (*p*) is recessive. Count the number of purple grains in 4 rows of the ear. Then find the number of yellow grains in the same 4 rows.

Divide the number of purple grains in 4 rows by the number of yellow grains in 4 rows. Is the answer closest to 1, 2, 3, or 4?

Are the yellow grains *PP, Pp,* or *pp*?

Are the purple grains *PP, Pp,* or *pp*? Can you tell by looking at the purple grains, which grains are *PP* or *Pp*?

The pollen and eggs that produced this ear of corn came from the same corn plant. Was the corn plant *PP, Pp,* or *pp*?

5. Are "two peas in a pod" really alike?

ADVENTURE 10

From Algae To Corn Plants

THE PLANT KINGDOM

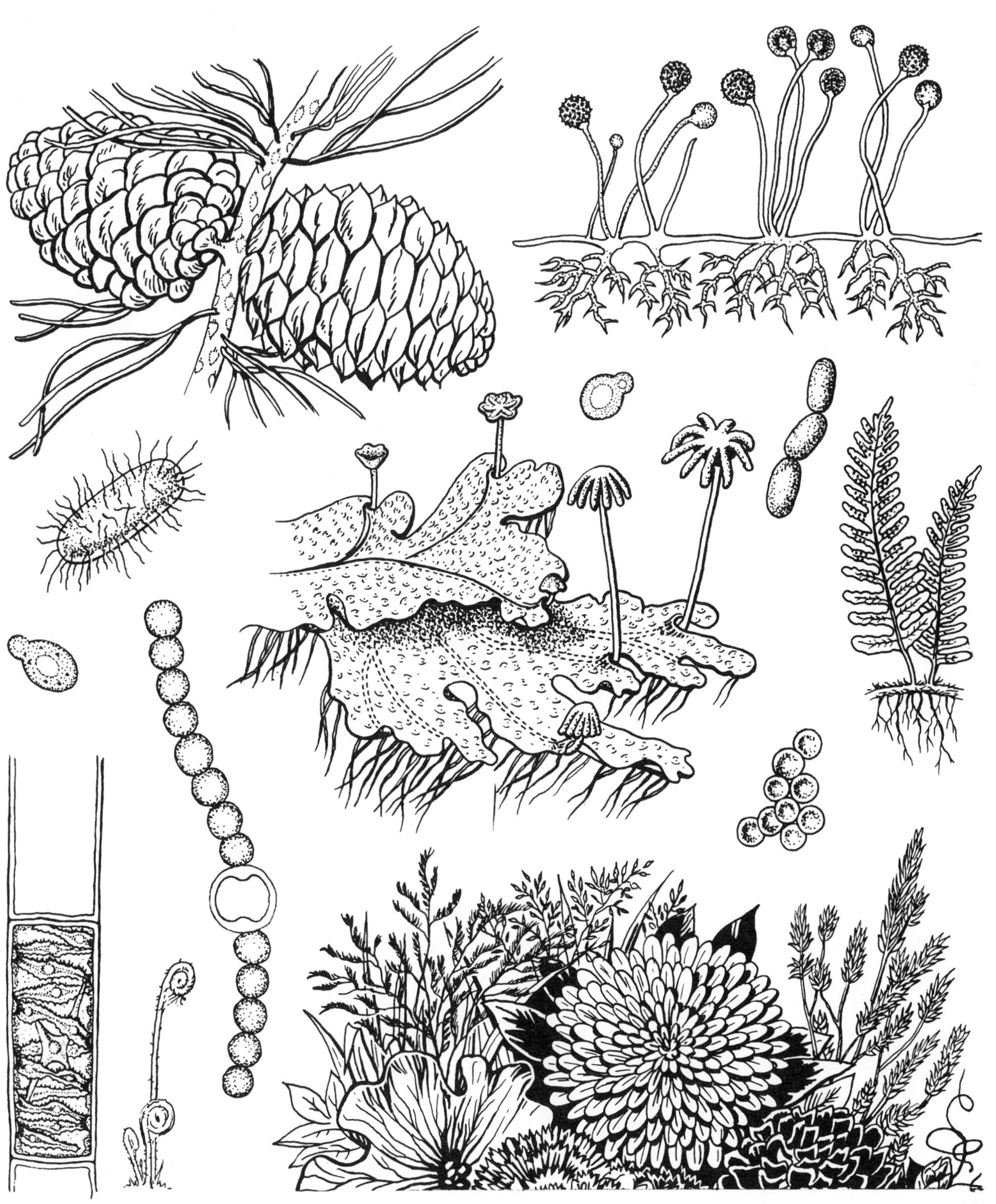

From Algae To Corn Plants

COME ON; climb aboard! I'd like to take you on a trip around the countryside! We'll go in my special supersonic microjet. We won't bother to visit any people on this trip; people all look about the same! Instead, we'll look at all the kinds of plants we can find. There are about 500,000 kinds to see so we have plenty to look at! You're right; we won't look at all 500,000 of them! But we can look at the main kinds. Are you ready? Let's blast off! Here we go!

Pretty nice jet plane I have, isn't it? This jet flies at supersonic speeds, but it does more than that. When I closed the cabin door a tricky thing happened! The jet plane, and we in it, automatically became very small! Right now the plane, you, and I are only the size of a pin-head! Now we can fly into very small places and get a good look! This plane is also made so it can go underwater like a submarine; and it has a rotary blade so we can fly in one spot, just like a helicopter!

Why don't we start our trip by visiting the simplest green plants, and then work up to the more complex plants? Ah, there are some of the simple green plants now! I'm sure you have heard of them before. You guessed it; they are *algae*. They're in that fresh-water lake right below us. I'll dive our plane into it so we can get a close look at a few million algae!

See those long threads of blue-green cells, the ones that look like beads of a necklace? They are *blue-green algae*. These algae look bluish-green because their cells have a special kind of chlorophyll in them. This special chlorophyll helps in photosynthesis just like ordinary chlorophyll, though. Watch, I'll show you how blue-green algae reproduce. I'll steer the plane right into that long thread

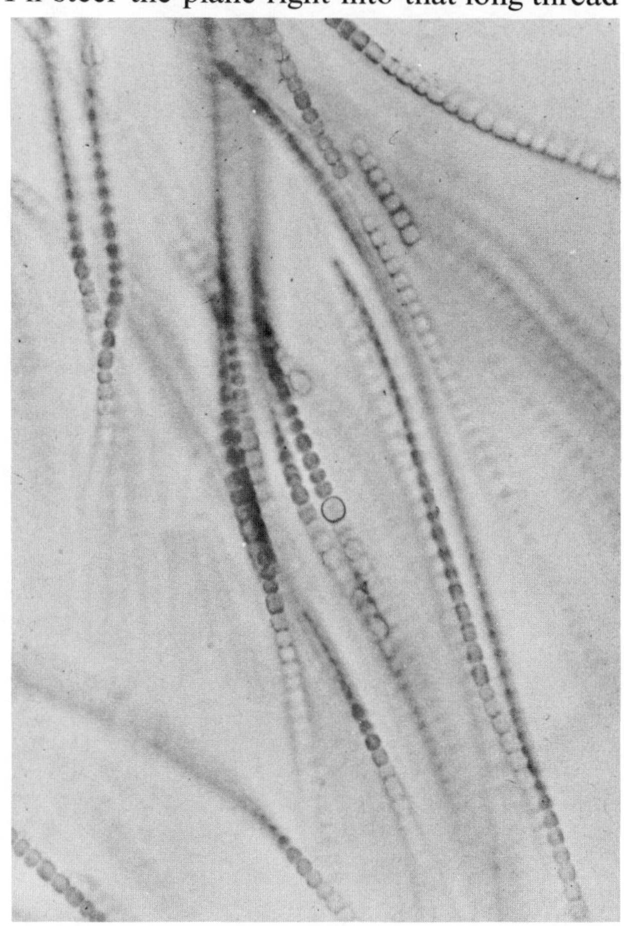

Long threads of blue-green algae.

of cells just ahead of us. Hang on! Here we go! Snip! See? We cut that thread of cells in two! Now watch the two short pieces. Pretty neat! The cells of each piece started dividing and growing as if nothing had happened! Now there are two long threads of cells. That is the simplest kind of reproduction found in plants. The long threads of cells break into small threads, and each piece grows into bigger pieces.

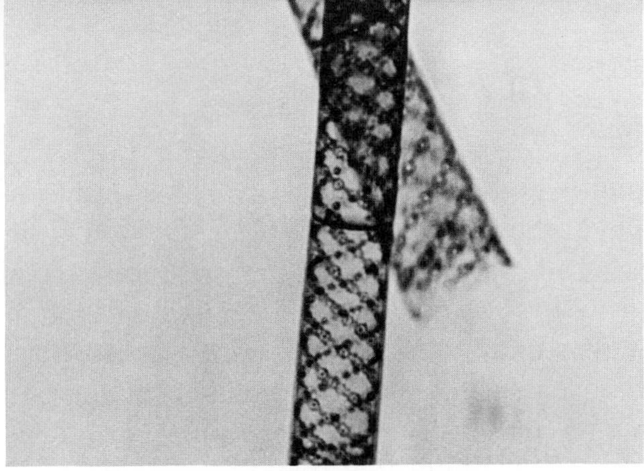

Spiral chloroplasts of *Spirogyra.*

Look out! Whew; that was close! Our ship almost got trapped in a clump of *green algae*! It would have been a job to get out of that! That clump is made of long, green threads of *Spirogyra*. See how green they are? And the chlorophyll in each cell is in a long, spiral chloroplast. Pretty, isn't it!

Say, we're in luck! I see another kind of green algae just ahead of us. It's *Oedogonium*. That's a real tongue-twister! Aren't you glad your name isn't *Oedogonium*! Anyway, it's an interesting green algae. Can you see its eggs and sperm cells? Look closely and you'll

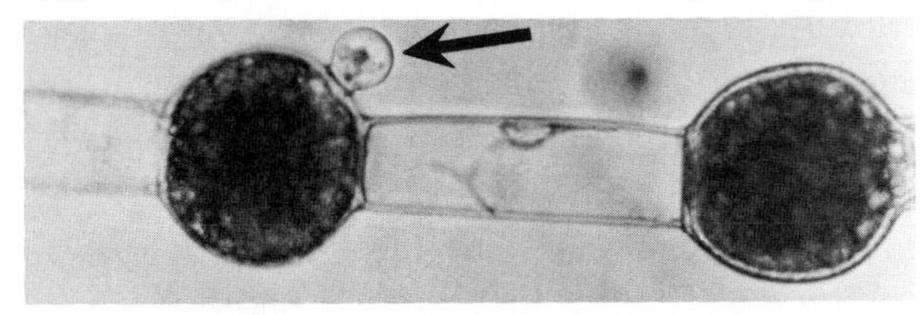

See the *sperm cell* fertilizing the egg?

see them. Those tiny cells swimming toward that big cell are sperm cells. And that big cell is an egg. A sperm cell will fertilize the egg. Then the fertilized egg will fall to the bottom of the pond and grow into a new thread of *Oedogonium* cells. You can see this kind of reproduction is something like the way flowering plants reproduce. Both kinds of plants have eggs and sperm cells. And the fertilized egg divides and grows into a new plant.

Now let's leave this lake and fly over the Pacific coastline. I'll show you some other kinds of algae growing in the salty water of the ocean. There they are! The tide has washed the algae onto the shore. The long, leafy, brownish plants are *brown algae*. Those brown algae can grow as long as a football field! They look brown because their cells contain a special kind of chlorophyll that is brown. Some people like to eat brown algae! The Japanese find brown algae very tasty. Don't laugh! You've eaten brown algae many times, too! Don't think you have, eh? Do you like ice cream? I thought so! Well, most ice cream has a substance in it that makes the ice cream smooth and creamy; that substance comes from brown algae!

See those small bits of reddish algae along the shore? Those are *red algae*. Yes, they have a special red chlorophyll in their cells. Brown algae and red algae both reproduce by eggs and sperm, the same as the green algae do.

Say, look over there! See that white hillside where some men are mining the white

A leafy, brown alga.

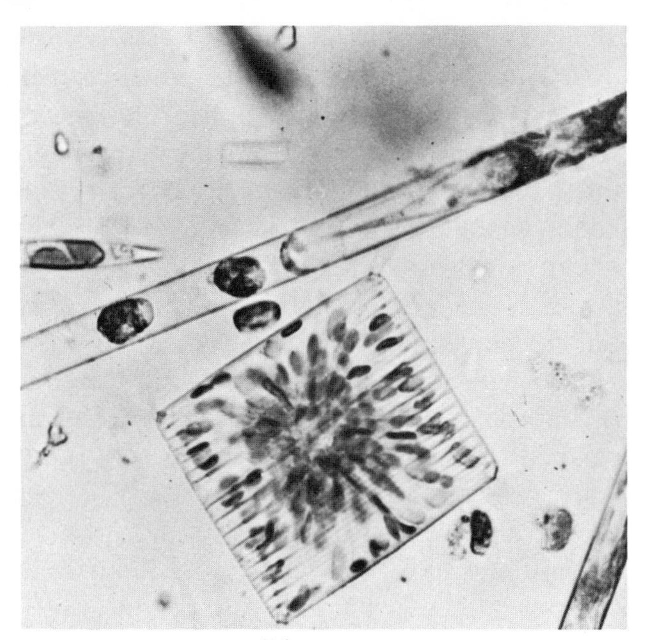

Diatoms.

rock? I think they are mining some fossil algae called *diatoms*. Let's dive down and take a closer look. That's it; they're mining diatoms. The hillside is made of countless billions of dead diatoms. The diatoms they are mining lived many years ago in an ancient ocean. When the diatoms died, they sank to the ocean bottom. There were so many dead diatoms they formed this thick layer of white rock. It took a long time to do that. Diatoms are used in many products, even toothpaste! There are many kinds of diatoms living today, too. Next chance you get, look at some diatoms under a microscope. They are really beautiful! Their cell walls are shaped and carved into designs more delicate than snowflakes. Even the fossil diatoms those men are mining still have the delicate designs. That's because the cell walls of diatoms contain silica, the same stuff sand and glass are made of. It is very hard, so the cell walls of the fossil diatoms still have the shape they did when they were alive thousands of years ago!

Well, so much for algae! Now let's look at plants that *don't* contain chlorophyll. Do you know what they are called? Good for you! They're the *fungi*! Fungi are quite different from most plants because they can't do photosynthesis. Since they can't make chlorophyll, they aren't green, either. Do you know where fungi get food for their respiration and growth? From dead organic matter such as leaves and stems? That's partly right! Many fungi can get their food from living organisms. Fungi that live on living things are called *parasites*. Fungi that live on dead things are *saprophytes*.

You have billions of parasites and saprophytes living inside you right now! There are billions and billions of *bacteria* living in your body. Some are good bacteria that help you digest food; some even make vitamins and other things your body needs. Most of these bacteria live in your large intestine. I hope you don't have too many of the harmful kind of bacteria that cause disease.

There's a rotting leaf! I think we'll find plenty of bacteria there to look at. See how tiny the bacterial cells are? If you could lay bacteria side by side, you would need over a million of them just to cover the head of a pin! How many different shapes of bacteria can you see? Do you see those round, ball-like bacteria? Those are *cocci*. Those cigar-shaped bacteria are *bacilli*. That wiggly thing which just swam past us is a bacillus; it has long, whiplike cilia. The cilia are like oars on a boat. They move back and forth in the water and that makes a bacillus move. We're

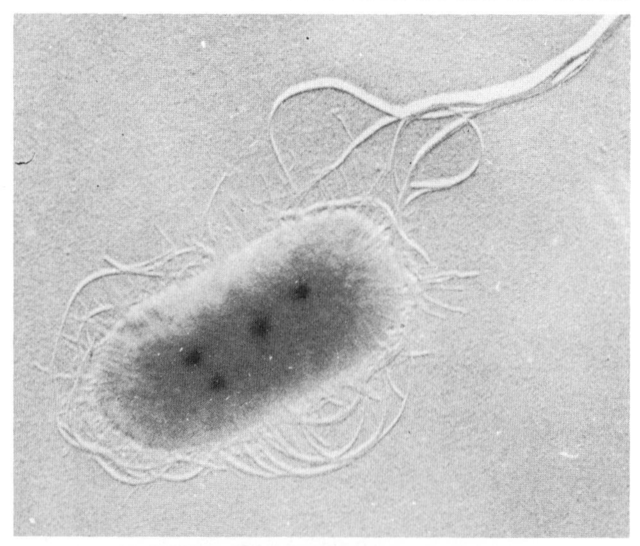

See the wiggly *cilia* of this *bacillus*?

in luck! I can see some *spirillum* bacteria. See those small cells that look like springs? Each one is a spirillum.

Many people believe all bacteria are harmful. Do you? Actually, very few kinds of bacteria are harmful. Most kinds of bacteria are very helpful and we need them. Those we just looked at in the decaying leaf are helpful bacteria. Without them, what would happen to all the dead leaves, stems, and other plant and animal remains formed each year? The dead matter would not rot and decay; it would accumulate, year after year! After a few years the earth would be covered with a thick layer of dead animals and plants! Wouldn't that be a mess! You can begin to see why we need helpful bacteria to decay dead things. There are many other kinds of helpful bacteria; some are in nodules of bean plants; also there are nitrogen-fixing bacteria, sulfur bacteria, and many others. You will want to find out more about them some other time!

Now we've seen some bacteria; maybe we can find some other types of fungi. There's one now! See those things that look like balls? I'll fly closer to them so you can get a better view. They are fruiting bodies of a *slime mold*. Those balls have spores inside them. Each spore is a single cell. Some of them will fall to the ground and start growing. They will grow into a slimy mass of cytoplasm that creeps over the wet ground. The slimy mass of cytoplasm may grow as large as a fifty-cent piece! Finally the slimy mass stops moving and forms these ball-shaped bodies. Each nucleus in the slimy mass becomes the nucleus of a spore. And the spore starts the life of the slime mold over again!

Slime mold balls have *spores* inside them.

Common bread mold on a tomato. Each black ball looks like a speck here, but contains thousands of spores.

Now I think we'll fly into a garbage can! That's not a very nice place to visit, but we'll find lots of fungi there. The odors from the decaying garbage can't get into our jet plane, so don't worry about the smell! Ah, there's a garbage can. Here we go! I'll turn on the plane's spotlight so we can see our way around. Can you see a moldy piece of food anywhere? Good! Let's take a close look at it.

Have you ever seen this mold before? I am sure you have. It's the common *bread mold*. Botanists call it *Rhizopus*. It belongs to a group of fungi that are all algae-like, except that their cells don't have any chlorophyll. See the large black ball on the top end of this long stalk? That black ball has thousands of black spores in it. The spores will fall onto the food and start to grow. A long tube-like cell grows out of each spore. It grows longer and longer. Finally it looks like a tangled mass of white stringy stuff on the top of the food.

These cells of the mold use the food for their respiration; they can't do any photosynthesis themselves. After a few hours or a day or two, long stalks grow up from the white mass of *Rhizopus*. The end of each stalk grows into a round ball, and spores are made inside it. Then the life of this algae-like fungus starts all over again.

Can you see any moldy oranges, lemons, or cheese? There's a lemon! It's covered with a blue-green mass of cells. Do you know what fungus it is?

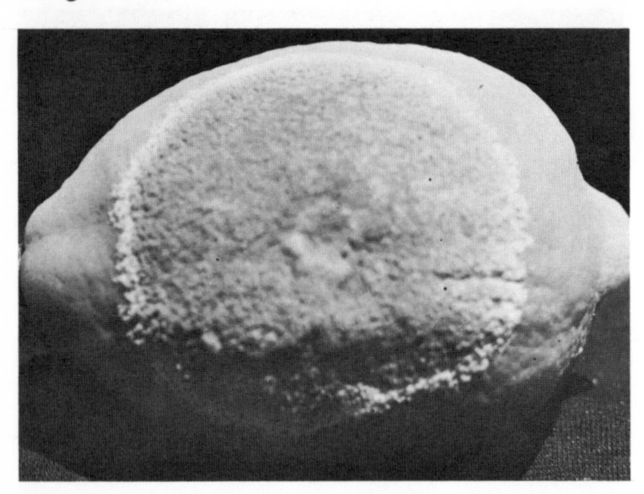

That's right! *Penicillium. Penicillium* is the mold that makes *penicillin.* Your doctor has probably shot some of it into your bottom! Penicillin is an *antibiotic,* which means it kills bacteria and other fungi. Why it doesn't kill *Penicillium,* the fungus that makes it, I don't know! *Penicillium* belongs to the *sac fungi.* These fungi were so named because one kind of spores they make is made inside a sac-like cell. The spores are like marbles inside a small bag. You can guess what each spore does. Right! Each spore can grow into another fungus plant.

While I think of it, your mother uses a sac fungus in the kitchen when she bakes bread and biscuits. Do you know the name of this fungus? That's it; yeast! You may know another kind of sac fungus. Do you have athlete's foot? Maybe you don't have this disease, but some of your friends may. Athlete's foot is caused by a sac fungus. Since the fun-

Let's fly under a mushroom's cap.

gus uses the living skin of your toes for food, it is a parasite.

So much for garbage cans and sore feet! Next stop, a forest! There will be lots of *club fungi* to see there! These fungi form spores on the end of very small club-like cells. That's why they're called club fungi. You have seen club fungi many times, so we won't stay long to look at them. Ah, there's one; a *mushroom.* You don't believe that's a mushroom? You think it's a toadstool? Well, we're both right! Mushrooms and toadstools are the same thing! Let's fly under the cap of the mushroom so we can see the gills. Beautiful aren't they? Millions of spores are formed on small clubs along the sides of those gills.

Look over there! It's a *puffball.* Did you ever step on one of them? If the puffball is ripe it explodes and clouds of blackish smoke fly out. Do you know what the smoke is? Well, it is millions and billions of colored spores. Each spore can grow into another puffball. Do you think many of the millions of spores in a puffball really do grow into more puffballs? Look! Over there! The bark of that tree is covered with *bracket* or *shelf fungi*. These fungi form spores on the ends of little clubs, just like puffballs and mushrooms, so they belong to the club fungi, too.

The bark has bracket or shelf fungi on it.

Now we've seen all the main groups of fungi. Let's get back to green plants!

See the mat of smooth, green plants on that hillside? It looks like a green carpet! Those plants are *mosses*. I'll fly close to them so we can see each tiny moss plant. Can you see each little leafy plant? Actually, mosses don't have real leaves, stems, and roots such as we have traveled in on other adventures. Mosses are primitive plants and they have only leaf-like, stem-like, and root-like parts. Botanists think mosses were the first plants to grow on land millions of years ago. That was before there were any trees, shrubs, or flowering plants such as we have today.

The life of a moss plant is more complex than the lives of the algae and fungi we just visited. Each of these tiny moss plants will form eggs and sperm cells at the top of the leaf-like plant. Then a sperm cell fertilizes an egg; the fertilized egg starts to grow. But it doesn't grow into a leafy moss plant! Instead it grows into a long stalk with a football-shaped thing on the top end of it. The football-shaped part is called a *capsule*. Can you see the stalks and capsules? Spores are formed inside the capsules. Each spore is a single cell like other spores we have talked about. When the capsule dries out, the spores roll out and fall to the ground.

Moss *spores* are inside the *capsules*.

Then the spores grow and become the leafy plants we call mosses.

There are several kinds of plants that are close relatives of mosses; we won't bother to look at them on this trip, though. They are the *liverworts* and *sphagnum*. You don't see liverworts very often, but you can buy sphagnum in most five- and ten-cent stores. Sphagnum is a moss-like plant that grows along the edge of some lakes and ponds. Many lakes in the northern United States and Canada have sphagnum growing in them. Sphagnum is taken from the lakes and put into bags and sold as "peat-moss." Of course, it really isn't a moss, but it is a close relative. Next time you see some peat-moss in a store, look at it closely. You'll see the leaf-like sphagnum plants.

Now let's look at plants that have real roots, stems, and leaves! But first let's look only for *seedless* plants with roots, stems, and leaves! I'll bet you didn't know there were any such plants. But stop and think for a moment; maybe you'll remember what plants they are. There's one growing near a clump of mosses. Surprised aren't you! It's a common

fern. Ferns and *their relatives* don't have flowers; and they don't form seeds. But ferns and relatives of ferns are more complex than mosses. That's because ferns and their relatives have true roots, stems, and leaves. They look like roots, stems, and leaves inside and out! They have xylem and phloem pipes just like the kind we traveled in on an earlier adventure inside a tree. Fern leaves look like the leaves we have walked through, too. Fern leaves even have stomates!

Do you know what part of a fern plant is the stem? If you look for it above ground, you won't find it! The stem of a fern grows underground. Instead of growing up in the air, it grows horizontally through the soil! The underground stem makes leaves as a stem should. Then the leaves grow upward and into the air above ground. So what most people call the "stem and leaves" of a fern is really only a leaf! Of course, fern roots grow from the stem down through the soil, just as roots should.

Now I'll steer the microjet plane up close to the fern leaf so we can see the underside of it. See those brown spots all over the underside of this fern leaf? It looks as if the leaf is covered with a fungus disease! But it isn't.

The fern plant isn't sick! Those brown spots are perfectly normal. Fooled you, didn't they? Each brown spot has thousands of spores in it. Each spore can fall to the ground and grow into a small, green plant. But this new green plant won't look like a fern at all. There are some of them! See those heart-shaped little plants on the wet ground? They are only about 1/8 of an inch wide! Those little plants are forming eggs and sperm cells. Each egg will be fertilized by a sperm. Then the fertilized egg will grow into a fern plant with roots, stems, and leaves.

Pine trees have two kinds of cones.

So much for plants *without* seeds! Now let's find some plants *with* seeds. But let's see if we can find plants with seeds that don't have flowers! Impossible? Not at all! If you stop and think for a moment, you'll know I'm talking about *pine trees* and their relatives. These plants have real roots, stems, leaves, and seeds, but they don't have flowers! How can there be seeds and no flowers? Let's find out! The pine trees of this forest will show us the answer.

Look up above us! See those small, yellow, *cones* near the tips of the pine branches? Those are *male* or *pollen-forming cones.* Millions of pollen grains are made inside them. I'll fly our plane past a male cone; watch the clouds of pollen grains blowing out of the cone. Now look way up high in the tree. See the large cones? You have seen them before, many times. Those are *female* or *seed-forming cones.* Let's zoom up there and take a closer look!

Female cones are made of many hard scales. Each scale forms two ovules. The two ovules lie on the top side of each scale. And each ovule has an egg cell in it. Wind carries the pollen from the male cone up to the female cone; then the pollen cell grows and forms a long pollen tube. The pollen tube grows into the ovule. Next a sperm nucleus from the pollen tube fertilizes the egg. The fertilized egg grows and becomes an embryo pine plant inside the seed. When the female cone opens, the seeds fall out of the cone onto the ground. If the seed gets wet and the days are warm, the embryo plant inside the seed will start to grow. It may become a new pine tree—if a squirrel doesn't eat it first!

So you see pine trees have cones and not flowers. And there are two kinds of cones; the male cones form pollen, and the female cones form eggs. Does it seem strange to you to have pollen made in one place and eggs in another? Really, it isn't so strange. Think about a corn plant. The ears that you eat are the female flowers. And what are the tassels of corn? Right! Tassels are groups of small flowers that form pollen! So even some plants which have flowers, have two kinds of flowers —male and female flowers.

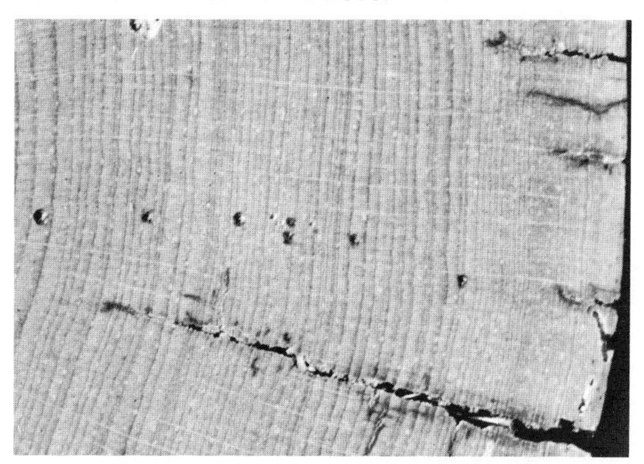

One ring of wood was formed each year.

I forgot to show you one very important part of a pine tree; a part that none of the algae, fungi, mosses, or ferns have! It's the *cambium.* If I can find a sawed-off tree stump I can show it to you. There's one! I'll dive down to the stump so you can see the cambium. Can you see the rings of wood in this tree stump? It took a year for the plant to grow each of those rings. This tree was very skinny when it was young. As it grew, a new ring of wood cells was made each year around its stem; slowly the stem got wider and wider. Only plants that have a special kind of cells can do this. The special cells are the cambium. The cambium is that ring of cells between the *wood* and the *bark*. Each year the cambium cells divide and form several new cells. Some of these cells become a new ring of wood (xylem). A few of the cells made by the cambium become new phloem cells in the bark. Of course, one ring of cells doesn't change into either phloem or xylem. It stays as cambium so more xylem and phloem can be made the next year! Now you can see that it is the cambium that makes lumber. Without the cambium, a tree would be thin and skinny; it wouldn't grow wide enough to be sawed into boards.

While we can see it, look at all that greenish fuzzy stuff on the branches and the bark of these pine trees. Do you know what that is? It is made of *lichens!* A lichen is really two plants in one! They live together! One of the plants is an alga; the other is a fungus. The algal cells are green and make food for themselves and the fungus. The fungus steals water from the pine tree for itself and the algal cells. And they live very happily this way! Each helps the other. There are many kinds of lichens. Some grow on trees and some grow on rocks. Next time you take a hike, look for them. I'm sure you'll see several kinds.

Lichen – two plants in one.

Well, it has been a long trip and we have seen many things. The only group of plants we haven't looked at on this trip is the flowering plants. But we have seen them many times before on our other adventures, so let's not bother with them right now.

As we head back for home, I'll make a list of the kinds of plants that we have visited. Can you fly the plane while I write the list? Good! Take over!

ALGAE

- *BLUE-GREEN* ALGAE

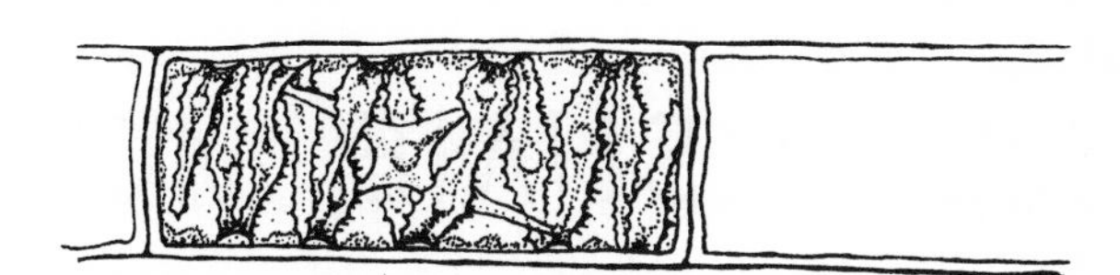

- *GREEN* ALGAE

- *BROWN* ALGAE

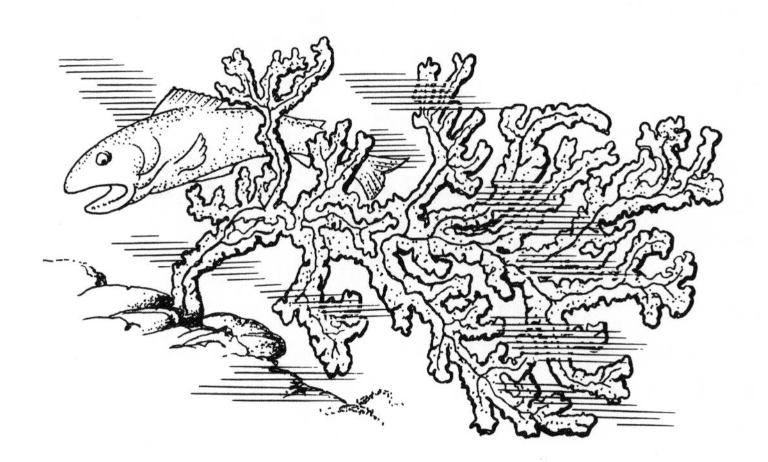

- *RED* ALGAE

- *DIATOMS*

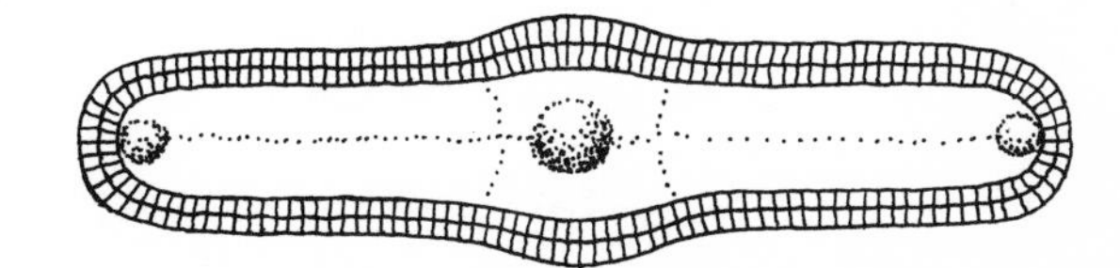

FUNGI

- *BACTERIA*

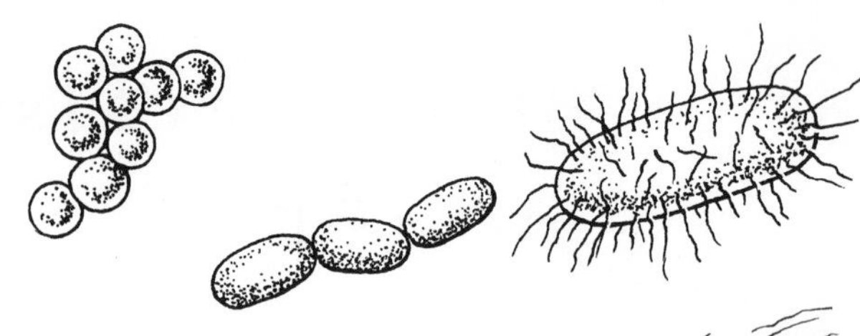

- *SLIME MOLDS*

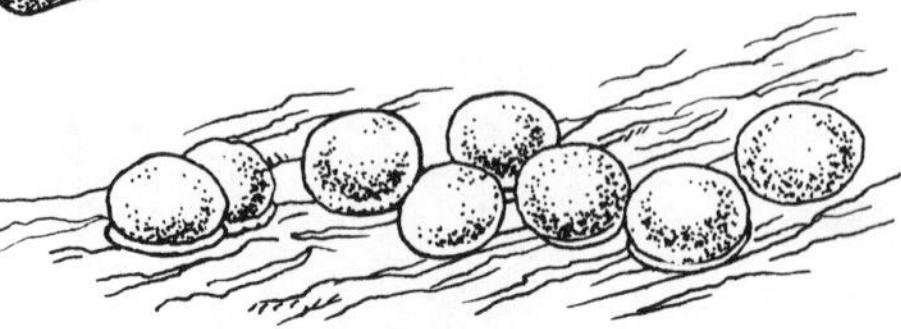

- *ALGAE-LIKE FUNGI*

- *SAC-FUNGI*

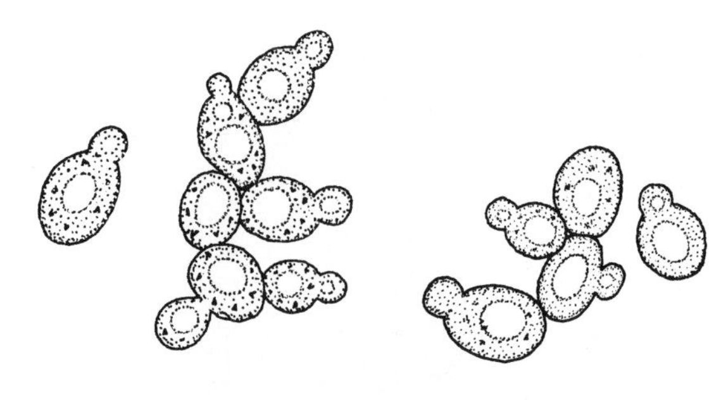

- *CLUB-FUNGI*

LICHENS

LIVERWORTS

MOSSES

SPHAGNUM

FERNS *and their Relatives*

SEED PLANTS

• *PINES and their Relatives*

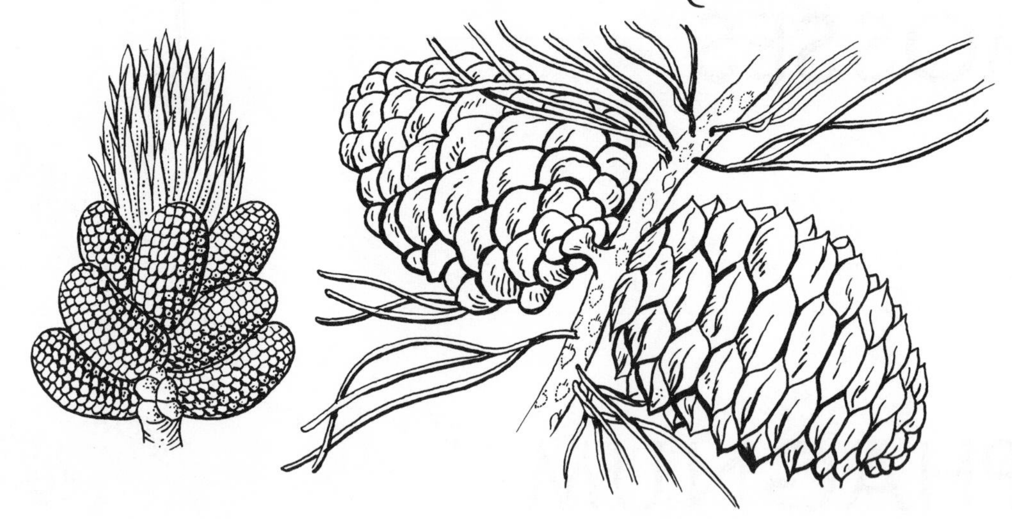

• PLANTS *with Flowers*

Things to Do and Think About

1. Collecting algae. Collect as many different algae as you can. Collect water and green scum from fish ponds, lakes, streams, from an aquarium, and from irrigation ditches. Also scrape the green algae off the bark on the north side of trees and from the sides of swimming pools. Many blue-green algae can be found on the surface of soil that has been moist for several days. If you live near the ocean, look for red, green, and brown algae in tide pools and along the shore. Also look for diatoms in toothpastes.

If you have a microscope, use it to look at the algae. Be sure to mount the algae in two or three drops of water on a slide, and cover the mount with a cover slip. You will be amazed at all the things you will see!

Large algae, such as seaweed, can be mounted on large sheets of heavy white paper. When the algae dry, they stick to the paper. Seaweeds should be washed with fresh, non-salty water before they are mounted on the paper.

Small algae from ponds, crusts of soil, etc., can be preserved, too. Use rubbing alcohol as the preservative. Put the algae in glass bottles, and add an equal volume of rubbing alcohol. Put the lid tightly on the bottle so the alcohol won't evaporate.

2. Collecting fungi. Make a collection of one or two kinds of fungi from each of the groups of fungi: bacteria, slime molds, algae-like fungi, sac fungi, and club fungi. You should look for fungi in moist decaying leaves and compost piles; on moldy bread, cheese, oranges, and fruits; in damp woods, in sour milk and rancid butter; on diseased plants; in stagnant ponds; on moldy dead insects; and inside nodules (little round balls) on the roots of bean, pea, soybean, clover, and other plants of the bean family. The more you look, the more fungi you will find! Fungi are all around you!

3. You can have fun making spore prints. If you can find several mushrooms, you can make some beautiful spore prints. When you gather the mushrooms, handle them carefully. With a knife, cut the stalk of the mushroom off just below the head and gills. Now set the mushroom head on a sheet of very white paper. The gills should be next to the paper. Moisten some newspaper; stick the moist paper against the inside of a large glass bowl. Now place the bowl upside-down over the white paper and mushroom head. Do not move the set-up for several hours. Then remove the bowl and mushroom head. Usually a beautiful print of the mushroom will be left on the paper. The print is made of millions of spores. The spores were formed on the sides of the gills. In the moist, still air inside the bowl, the spores fell to the paper. The designs and colors of the spore prints are used to help identify the mushroom.

Make spore prints of all the kinds of mushrooms you can find. You will be surprised at the many colors of spore prints that you get. You may want to use black paper instead of white paper; you will find that some spores are white.

Scrape some of the spores on to a glass microscope slide; add a drop of water; stir the mixture and put a cover slip on the mount. Now look at the spores through a microscope. It is hard to believe that each spore contains all the recipe for making another mushroom!

4. Collecting sick plants. Make a collection of plant diseases. Here are some diseases to look for:

Club root of cabbage – fat short roots of cabbage.

Bread mold – black mold on old moist bread or tomato.

Blisters and scabby areas on bean pods, potatoes, and soft stems

Chestnut stem blight

Diseases of leaves – tobacco and tomato mosaic virus spots; peach leaf curl; powdery mildews on shrubs; elm tree blight

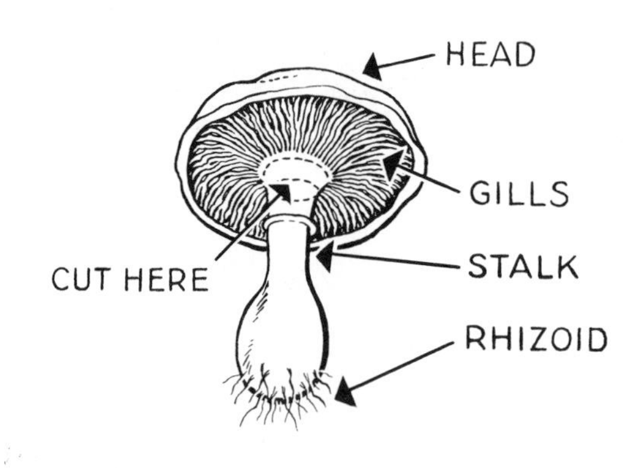

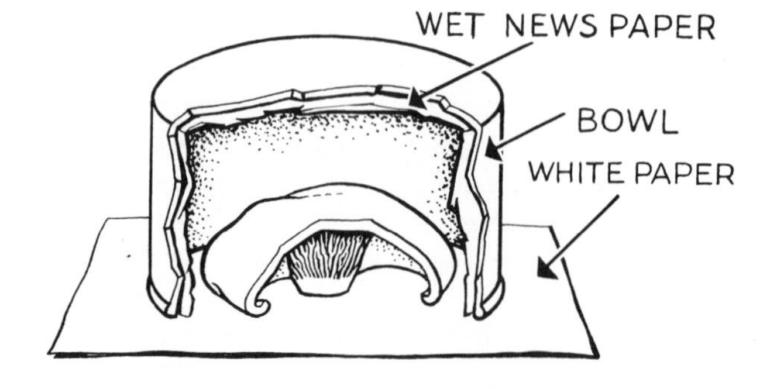

Diseases of fruits—soft rot of peaches; brown rot of plums; ergot of rye; black smuts in ears of corn and heads of wheat, oats, and other grasses
Rust of wheat stems
Cedar apples on cedar trees

Most encyclopedias show pictures of these diseases. There are excellent books on plant diseases in most libraries. And most state colleges of agriculture have free bulletins on plant diseases. The bulletins from your state college will tell about the diseases found in your state; write your state college of agriculture for information and bulletins about plant diseases. Your agricultural county agent will be glad to help you identify plant diseases, too. If you live near a university or state college, arrange a visit with the Department of Plant Pathology. A plant pathologist will gladly show you how they study and identify plant diseases.

5. *An experiment with milk.* Get four test tubes that are about six inches long and one-half inch wide. Clean them with lots of soap and warm water. Put a small piece of tape on the side of each clean tube; number the tubes #1, 2, 3, and 4. Fill each tube with fresh milk to within 1/2 inch of the top of the tube. Next put a piece of rich garden soil into tubes #2 and 4; the piece of soil should be about the size of a pea seed. Fold a small piece of aluminum foil over the top of tubes #1 and 2. Plug the opening of tubes #3 and 4 with modeling clay. The milk in tubes #3 and 4 should come up to the clay so that no air is between the milk and clay.

Stand the four tubes inside a glass in a warm place. Look at the tubes every day for five days. Does the milk look different in each tube during the five-day culture period? Can you see any difference between the tubes with soil (#2 and 4) and the tubes without soil (#1 and 3)? Do the tubes that are aerobic (#1 and 2) look any different from the tubes that are anaerobic (#3 and 4)?

After five days, carefully remove the clay plugs and aluminum foil caps. Put the plugs and caps in the garbage. Now smell the odor of each tube. Do you like the smell? Which tubes have the strongest odor? The odor is butyric acid ($C_4H_8O_2$). Butyric acid is an end-product of the anaerobic respiration of milk fats by bacteria. The bacteria were in the soil. Sometimes milk has these bacteria, too.

Carefully pour the contents of the four tubes down the drain. Wash your hands and the tubes with lots of soap and warm water.

If you can get some raw milk (milk that has not been pasteurized), try this experiment again; but this time fill tubes #2 and 4 with raw milk. Put pasteurized milk in tubes #1 and 3. Do not put soil in any of the tubes. Look at the tubes and smell them after five days.

What is pasteurization?

6. *Let's grow some fungi.* Try growing some fungi on bread, oranges, pieces of pumpkin fruit, cheese, peaches, open grapes, etc. First get the food you want to use. Then get several drinking glasses and dishes;

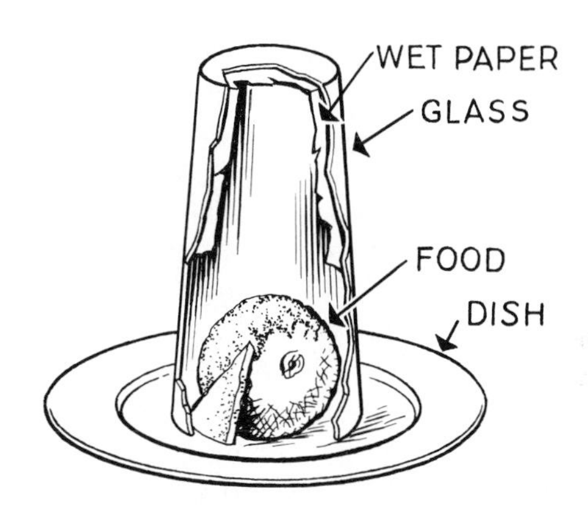

The glass should be large enough to fit over the piece of food. Put some wet newspaper on the inside of each glass. Then put a piece of food in each dish and cover the food with a glass.

Put the set-ups in a dark cabinet or closet for several days. Look at the food each day. After a few days you should have good, moldy growths on most of the food. If the food isn't moldy, do this: wet the newspapers again; leave the food uncovered for an hour; cover the food with the glass; wait a few more days. Usually these fungi will grow on each food:

bread and pumpkin—*Rhizopus* (bread mold)
cheese, oranges, fruits in general—*Penicillium* (green mold) and *Aspergillus* (black mold that doesn't have the large black spore-containing bodies that *Rhizopus* has)
open grapes—yeasts

Look at the fungi with a hand lens or through a microscope. Can you see the spores? Can you see the long threadlike cells of *Rhizopus* and *Penicillium?* Can you smell the odor of alcohol coming from the rotting grapes? Does the odor tell you what kind of fungus is growing in the grapes?

Large, moldy growths on bread and fruit can be preserved in bottles in rubbing alcohol.

7. *Collecting lichens.* Find all the kinds of lichens that you can. Look for lichens on trees, wet or dry rocks, decaying logs, and pasture soils. See how many differ-

ent shapes and colors of lichens you can find. You can keep lichens if you store them in a dry place.

Do you find certain kinds of lichens always growing on certain kinds of trees or types of rock? Can you suggest how come?

8. Collecting mosses. Collect some mosses with capsules. Look at them with a hand lens. Can you see the leaf-like green parts that carry on photosynthesis? Can you find the root-like parts that take in water and minerals from the soil? Crush a capsule on a piece of glass. Were there any spores inside the capsule?

9. Let's look at ferns. Get a living fern plant. Can you find the underground stem? Do you see the roots and leaves growing from the stem? Cut the stem across with a knife; look at the cut surface with a hand lens. Can you see cells that look like plumbing pipes (xylem)?

Find some fern leaves that have brown dots on their underside. Look at these dots with a hand lens or microscope. Can you see the little ball-like objects in which the spores are formed? Scrape some of these spore-forming balls on to a glass slide. Gently smash them against the glass; add a drop of water and cover slip; look at the spores under a microscope.

Make a collection of ferns. Press each fern flat between a sheet of newspaper that has been folded in half; put a couple of empty newspapers between each newspaper that has a fern. The newspapers and plants should form a neat pile. Put some heavy books on top of the pile of newspapers and ferns for a week or two. Put this plant press in a dry, warm place. If the ferns are moist when you collect them, the empty newspapers should be replaced with dry newspapers every other day. When the ferns are dry, you can mount them on large sheets of heavy, white paper. Narrow pieces of clear, plastic tape can be used to hold the ferns on to the paper. In the lower right-hand corner of the paper, write a complete label. A complete label should tell the following:

Name of fern, if known.
Where collected (place, county, and state).
Habitat (kind of soil it was growing in; kind of plants growing near the fern).
Date collected.
Name of person who collected the fern.

This information, except the name of the fern, should be recorded in a field notebook at the time you collect the fern. Most libraries have books on ferns that will help you to identify them.

10. Collecting pines and their relatives. Find some male and female cones of pine trees or their close relatives. Male cones usually fall off the tree in late spring and don't appear again until the next spring. Can you see the yellow pollen come out of a male cone when you shake it or crush it? Mount some pollen in water on a slide; put a cover slip over the mount; now look at the pollen under a microscope. Pollen grains of pines and their relatives have very distinct shapes.

Break a female cone apart. Can you find any seeds in it? How many seeds or ovules does each "leaf" of the female cone have? Cut a seed open; find the embryo. Does the embryo have more than two cotyledons?

Find a cut stump of a pine tree; look at the cut surface with a hand lens. Can you see the tree rings? Look at the layer between the wood and the bark. This layer is the *cambium;* it is a very thin layer. The cambium makes new cells each year; some new cells become wood (xylem) and some become phloem in the bark.

Look closely at a tree ring. Which part of the ring was made first, the part toward the center of the stem or the part toward the outside of the stem? Which part of the ring has larger cells? When does a pine tree use the most water, in the spring and early summer when it is growing fast or in the late summer and fall when it is growing slowly? Are all tree rings the same size (width)? Why are some rings wider than others? Does the width of a ring tell you something about the conditions in which the tree was growing when the rings were formed?

Make a collection of branches of all the kinds of pines and their relatives that you can find. Try to find branches of spruce, fir, gingko, juniper, larch, hemlock, cedar, cycads, and cypress. Follow the directions for collecting, pressing and mounting plants given in Experiment 9. Always collect male and female cones if they are available. You can find many books in libraries on identification of pine trees and their relatives. Encyclopedias are helpful, too.

11. Collecting flowering plants. Make a collection of different kinds of flowering plants. Include grasses, trees, garden plants, weeds, etc., in your collection. Always include roots, stems, leaves, and flowers of the plant you are collecting. Collect seeds and fruits, too, if they are available.

Press and mount the plants as described in Experiment 9. Books on identification of wildflowers, trees, and shrubs can be found in most bookstores and libraries. Encyclopedias are also helpful.

If you collect good specimens, dry them quickly and thoroughly, mount them neatly on clean paper, and label each mounted plant neatly and completely, you will have a good-looking plant collection. It will be a collection you can be proud of!

ADVENTURE 11
Plants And Their Surroundings
ECOLOGY

Imagine yourself standing in your front yard 10,000 years ago . . .

. . . What do you see? Are there cars? Are there airplanes flying overhead? Do you see houses, streets, and things invented by man in modern times? What about dogs, cats, horses, and other domestic animals? Do you see any of them 10,000 years ago? You're right!

You see some animals that might be their ancient relatives; but these ancient relatives don't look quite like the animals you know in the twentieth century. These relatives of our domestic animals don't seem very tame or friendly, either, so be careful!

Can you see any of the strange animals that were common in the United States 10,000 years ago? Giant, elephant-like mastodons with long tusks roamed over most of the United States! There were sabre-toothed tigers, too. And ground sloths! Can you see any of them? Say; there's a strange looking two-legged animal carrying a spear! Oh! It's a man! He's hunting a giant mastodon. He must be very brave to hunt such a monster with just a spear!

What do the sky and sun look like 10,000 years ago? The sun seems to be as bright as in the twentieth century, doesn't it? But the sky is cloudy and you feel rather cold for this time of year. You can see there has been lots of rain; everything is very damp. The summers and winters must be cooler and wetter than they will be 10,000 years later in the 1960's.

And look at the plants! They aren't the same as the ones that will be in your front yard 10,000 years from now! The grasses are tall and dense. The trees and shrubs are large and there are a lot of them. Why, some of these plants won't grow within 500 miles of your home in the twentieth century! The plants sure are different!

Look carefully at the plants and animals in your front yard 10,000 years ago. Are you wondering what changes will happen in the next 10,000 years? Why is it so cool and wet in 8,000 B.C.? Why do large grasses and trees grow here, and yet different kinds of plants will grow here 10,000 years from now? You can be sure of one thing: there will have to be many changes! Climate, animals, plants, the soil, and man will all change.

Some changes will be rather fast. Some will be slow. Mastodons, sabre-toothed tigers, and ground sloths won't be alive on earth in the 1960's. Can you guess why? That's right! The climate will slowly get drier and warmer during the next 10,000 years. This will cause the descendants of these animals to die, one by one. As the climate gets drier and warmer there may not be enough water for them to drink. Or they may not get enough grass and food to eat.

Do you know why there won't be enough food for these animals between now and 1960? There will still be some shrubs and grasses. But if you could watch the plants during the next 10,000 years, you would see them change, too. It is cool and wet now, in 8,000 B.C. Glaciers of ice have covered much of the earth; now they are melting and retreating to the north. As the glaciers melt, there will be a lot of rain. Then, slowly, as the climate gets warmer and warmer, it will also get drier. The kinds of plants growing on each part of the earth will change. Trees will slowly die in some places that get too dry and warm. Some places will become deserts. Seeds of other plants will sprout and take the place of the dead trees. But these new plants and their offspring must be able to grow and make seeds in the dry and warm climate. If the climate gets too dry and warm for them, these new plants will also die.

So there will be many trials and errors in the struggle for survival. As the climate of a place changes, some plants and animals won't be able to live there and reproduce. They will die and disappear from the area. Some of the animals may be able to move to a better place. But any animals that do not find a good place to grow and reproduce, will die. Birds will carry seeds of some plants from one place to another. Streams will carry some seeds many miles. Spores will blow in the wind. There will be many trials and errors; many kinds of plants and animals will start to live in many places. But only the plants and animals that can live and reproduce in a place will live there for very long. When the climate changes again, other kinds of plants and animals may come and take their places. That is what will happen to these mastodons and to the other animals enjoying life now in 8,000 B.C. The climate will change; the grasses and other plants will change; and these animals will die. They won't be able to find a place where there is enough food to keep them alive. So they will disappear from the earth! And these men with spears, hunting and killing mastodons. They're helping the mastodons disappear, too.

This struggle to survive has gone on for many, many years; in fact, for as long as there has been life on earth! Dinosaurs, mastodons, and thousands of other kinds of animals have come and gone. Many kinds of plants have come and gone, too. Do you know what a fossil hunter is? That's a person who likes to hunt for fossils. Well, fossil hunters have found hundreds of fossilized plants that don't look like any of the plants living in the twentieth century!

I can see you are puzzled about where all the different kinds of plants and animals have come from. How did each kind get started? Men have wondered about that for centuries! Let's think about it for a while, too.

You *MIGHT* think every kind of plant and animal was alive when living things first got started on earth. Then, as the climate changed over the years, some of these animals and plants died. Some were able to live and have offspring year after year. You *MIGHT* think the kinds of plants and animals alive in the twentieth century are the descendants of the ones that were able to survive year after year from the beginning. That is one way of thinking about it! Many people have thought that is the way things did happen.

But paleontologists say *NO!* Fossil hunters say that fossils tell a different story about life on earth. Let me ask you a question! Suppose every kind of plant and animal ever to live on earth was alive when life first got started; what kinds of rocks would have the most kinds of fossils in them? Would old rocks or young, recently-formed rocks have the most kinds of fossils? Which do you think would have the most kinds? Of course; the old rocks! It seems that the most fossils would be in very old rocks. You should be able to find fossils of almost every kind of plant and animal alive today in the oldest rocks. Do you know if that is what fossil-hunters really find? Right again! That is *NOT* what fossil-hunters find! There aren't many

Petrified tree stems are a kind of fossil.

kinds of fossils in the oldest rocks. And the fossils in the oldest rocks don't look like the plants and animals alive in the 1960's. What about young rocks, which have formed recently? What kinds of fossils do they have in them? It's just as you would expect; young rocks have fossils that look about like the plants and animals alive in the twentieth century! In fact, many of them look exactly like the plants and animals alive in the 1960's!

Most biologists and geologists believe simple organisms were the first living things on earth. These first living things probably had one simple cell! These cells probably looked like the blue-green algae we saw on our last adventure. They lived in the ocean. Can you guess how long ago these simple things lived? They lived about one billion years ago! Maybe even longer ago! One billion years—that's a long time! The fossil record tells us that algae with many cells came next. Later came mosses, then ferns, pine trees and their relatives, and still later the flowering plants. All this didn't happen overnight! It's almost unbelievable! The first flowering plant wasn't formed until *only* 150 million years ago! It took about 850 million years to go from simple algae to the first flowering plant!

I can see you are bothered by what I just said! How were these different kinds of plants "formed?" Did each kind all of a sudden appear? How did it happen? How was the first flowering plant formed? One thing we can be sure of; no one was there to see it happen 150 million years ago! No one was there to watch the algae, mosses, ferns, and other kinds of plants get "formed" either! We can only make a guess at how all the plants were formed! The same guess applies to animals, too. Let me tell you what most biologists think is the best guess about how plants and animals were formed.

Hand me some of that mud from where you are standing. Thanks! This mud doesn't look like much, does it? It's just a pile of mud. Now I'll slowly press the mud here and there with my fingers. Its shape is changing, isn't it? But the mud still doesn't look like much. A few more pokes and changes with my fingers are needed. Whoops! I pushed the mud too hard there. I'll smooth that place over! Watch closely! The mud is beginning to take shape. Just a few more pokes here—and a few more there. What does the pile of mud look like now? Right! The mud is shaped like a moss plant!

I'm sure you're wondering what mud has to do with how plants were formed! I don't blame you! Let me try to explain. The pile of mud you gave me didn't have any real shape, did it? Then I started poking and shaping the mud. You saw the shape of the mud change slowly. Some of the pokes I made in the mud weren't any good, so I got rid of them. I poked the mud some more. Slowly the mud took shape. Finally it looked like a moss plant.

Let's imagine the pile of mud stands for the first living cell. And imagine each poke I made in the mud stands for an inherited change of the cell. Some of the inherited changes, or pokes in the mud, were good changes. I let them remain! Other inherited changes, or pokes in the mud, were bad changes. So I erased them and got rid of the bad changes! After many small changes in the shape of the mud, it began to have a real shape. I made a few more small changes, some good, some bad. Finally the mud looked like a moss plant. You watched a pile of mud, or the first living cell, change into the shape of a moss plant. Each change was small and didn't make the mud look much different. But after many, many of these small changes, the mud looked very different!

The first living plant didn't look like much. It probably didn't have any more definite shape than a pile of mud! Then the first living plant reproduced; and generation after generation of plants reproduced. As they reproduced, some of the offspring looked a little different. If we remember about heredity, we should expect the offspring to look a little different. There were many inherited changes. Most of these inherited changes were very small. But sometimes there were large changes called *mutations*. Some of the small and large changes were good changes that let the offspring live and grow better. Other offspring had bad inherited changes. They couldn't grow well at all. Can you guess what happened to these offspring? Sure! They died or weren't able to reproduce! Slowly each generation of living plants changed. After many changes, the offspring began to look different from each other.

Now there were two kinds of plants! After many more changes, offspring from these plants looked different. Now there were three kinds of single-celled plants. This went on and on for millions of years! You'll agree that's plenty of time for many changes to take place! Especially since a single cell can reproduce every hour!

Sometimes the climate changed, too. When that happened, many kinds of plants died. If the new climate didn't agree with them, they died. But some other kinds of plants liked the new climate, so they lived and reproduced. Some of the inherited changes made one-celled plants become plants with many cells. These plants still lived in the oceans. More inherited changes in these plants made it possible for some of them to live along the ocean shore. After many, many more changes, the offspring of these plants were able to live on moist land. These were the first plants to live on land! They probably were moss-like plants. These moss-like plants were much different from the first living plant. Each change had been small. But there had been many of these small changes. It took 500 million years to get enough of these changes to form the moss plant!

And so it went, one kind of plant gradually changing into a new kind. This went on and on, generation after generation. The struggle was long and slow! The descendants of some kinds of plants lived; others died. Now, after one billion years of these changes, we have 500,000 kinds of living plants to look at. That's one new kind of plant every 2000 years! It seems like a giant step from the first living cell to the plants of today. But think of the millions of small steps that made the first plant change into all the modern plants. Then you'll see there really wasn't a giant step!

Try thinking of this, for comparison. Think about a modern jet transport plane; a four-engine plane, sleek in appearance, very large, and filled with motors, wires, and complicated dials and machinery. Now put the plane that the Wright brothers flew next to this jet plane. Their plane was simple, small, had one small engine, and it could fly only a few feet. It seems impossible! How could the modern jet plane be formed from the Wright brothers' plane in only 60 years? Yet we all know it was!

Many small changes had to be made to change the Wright brothers' plane into a modern jet plane. There were many trials and errors. Some of the planes flew; others crashed or never got off the ground! Some blew up! Changes in design that made the planes fly better were kept. Changes that didn't work were discarded. Slowly, one small change after another, the plane made by the Wright brothers became the modern jet plane. Unbelievable, but true! And it took only 60 years! Now jet planes are changing into rockets and satellites. It is a good thing pictures of these changes are put in history books and that out-dated planes are "fossils" in museums! After a few more years it will be almost impossible to believe it all started with the

"Kitty Hawk" made by the Wright brothers!

So much for the history of plants! Now let's take a look at the future! Is there a patch of weeds anywhere near your home? Even a small patch the size of a table top will do. There is? Good! You lead the way to it!

You're probably wondering why I want to look at weeds. We've been talking about changes in plants that have gone on for millions of years. But do all changes take millions of years? Do you think we can see changes in plants in a year's time? Or a month's time? Or a week's time? Well, that's why we want to look at a patch of weeds. Here we can see changes each month and week; we can even see some changes each day! I'll show you!

First, let's use this string to mark off one square meter of this weed patch. There! Now we have a definite area of ground to study and to watch.

What kinds of plants are growing in this patch? It doesn't really matter if we don't know their names! We can give each kind of plant a code number. We'll begin with Number 1. After we find out how many kinds of plants there are, then we want to find how many of each kind there are. It's like finding how many Smith's or Joneses there are in a city! We are taking the census of plants in one square meter! Be careful not to overlook tiny plants and seedlings. They want to be counted too!

Now that we have found the number of each kind of plant, we are ready to watch things change. We know what kinds and how many of each kind are there today. Will we find the same kinds and number of each kind tomorrow? Will we find some new seedlings tomorrow? Will some of the plants alive today be dead tomorrow? Perhaps there won't be much change by tomorrow. Perhaps it will be several days before we see changes in numbers and kinds of plants. But we will find changes after a while, of that I'm sure. Do you know why? Stop and think about all the things plants need in order to grow. Then you'll see why we will find changes sooner or later.

Do plants need light to grow? Do all plants need the same amount of light? Do plants need water to grow? Will a flood of water uproot a seedling or wash seeds away? Will a frost kill plants? Are all kinds of plants killed by a frost? Will wet, moldy soil cause some seeds and seedlings to rot and die? Can a stem live and grow if a rabbit comes by and

A weed patch is a good place to observe plant changes.

eats the stem tip for lunch? Can leaves do photosynthesis very well if insects chew on them or suck juice out of them? Can one plant affect the growth of another plant? Can a tall plant shade shorter plants so the short plants can't grow very well? Can the large roots of a large plant rob nearby smaller plants of soil water? You can see that life in this weed patch is a constant struggle. It is a quiet struggle few people stop to think about. There is no noise, no fuss, no cries of pain! But each plant is always struggling with its surroundings.

If you watch this weed patch for several weeks or months, you will see the outcome of this struggle, at least the outcome for this year! Some plants will be winners of this struggle to get light, water, soil, minerals and other needed things. The winners will not be diseased or harmed by animals and weather. These winners will grow well and will produce many seeds. There will also be some plants that are not real winners; but they aren't losers, either. These half-winners will struggle along not getting everything they need in the right amount. They will barely get by. At times some of these half-winners will be just about dead! But finally they will form a few seeds. There are also the losers of life's struggle to live and reproduce. The losers won't grow long enough or won't be healthy enough to form seeds.

As you look at this patch of weeds, can you tell which plants are going to be winners, half-winners, and losers? That's right! You can't! Plants, and animals, can't control their surroundings. So it is chance or "luck" which plants will be winners, half-winners, or losers. A plant can't tell an insect: "Please, don't eat my leaves! I need them for photosynthesis!" If an insect happens to come by this unlucky plant, the insect will nibble on the plant's leaves if it wants to. The plant can't stop the insect from doing this. And a plant can't make it rain when the soil gets dry and the plant is dying from lack of water. Or suppose a plant is just starting to make some seeds when a frost comes along. Do you think the plant can keep the frost from freezing its leaves and flowers? I should say not! Nothing, not even man, can control the weather! And a plant can't tell another plant: "Move over, your roots are getting in the way of my roots; you're stealing all the water!"

I think you can see it really is a matter of luck whether a plant will be a winner, half-winner, or loser. A plant that seems to be on its way to be a winner today, may be a loser tomorrow when a dog runs by and cracks the plant's stem! A plant that seems sure to be a loser because it is diseased with a fungus, may become a half-winner. The sun may shine brightly and cause the fungus to dry up and die. And now the fungus is a loser in the struggle to live and reproduce!

This is the way life's struggle has been going on for millions of years. It is a struggle that is fun to watch and study. Of course, let's not forget the inherited changes that occur while this struggle is going on. Some of these inherited changes may help a plant or animal to win the struggle for life. But some of these inherited changes can help a plant or animal to be a loser. It is a matter of luck what kind of inherited changes a plant or animal gets. No plant or animal can choose the kind of changes it inherits!

So year after year, season after season, day after day, the struggle goes on. It will continue to go on. There are many small inherited changes; there are some mutations or large changes; there are many losers; and there are a few winners. The struggle is going on all around us. You need only open your eyes to see nature's drama! But watch closely and carefully, with thought and understanding. Some parts of the struggle of life are easy to see and understand. Other parts of the struggle are easy to see, but hard to understand. Still other parts of the struggle are hard to see and still harder to understand. It's amazing, but most parts of the struggle of life aren't understood! The unknown parts are *frontiers in biology;* these frontiers are large and there are many of them. Biologists are pioneers as they explore these frontiers! Each frontier holds many exciting adventures. Would you like to be a pioneer biologist and explore these frontiers?

Yes, it's the same place! You can tell by the mountains in the background. The top picture was taken in 1903; the bottom picture was taken in 1964. See how the plant life has changed in the sixty-one years between the dates of the two pictures.

Things to Do and Think About

1. Fossil hunting. Try to find some fossils of plants and animals near where you live. Soft coal is a good place for you to look for fossils of plants. It is best to crack the coal apart; it will often crack where a fossil plant is. Limestone cliffs are also good sources of fossils; they are usually animal fossils of corals, snails, trilobites, and clams. Shales sometimes have fossils. A visit to a geological museum in your area will give you many ideas about where to look for fossils. If you can't find any fossils, read about them in books at your city library.

2. Does heat make plants grow faster? Get two or three different kinds of seeds. Count three groups of each kind of seed; there should be 25 seeds in each group. Put each group of 25 seeds in a separate glass of water for one hour.

Prepare three set-ups for seed germination as shown and described in Experiment 2 of Adventure 1. Soak the seeds for an hour, then spread 25 of each kind of seed in each of the three germination set-ups. Now each set-up should have two or three kinds of seeds in it, and there should be 25 soaked seeds of each kind. Wrap each germination set-up in aluminum foil. Then put one germination set-up in a refrigerator; put the second germination set-up at room temperature; put the third set-up in the warmest place you can find in your home or school. You can make a very warm place by hanging an incandescent light close to the germination set-up which is wrapped in aluminum foil. The light should be about 100 watts in size, hang about six inches from the top of the germination set-up, and be on all the time, day and night.

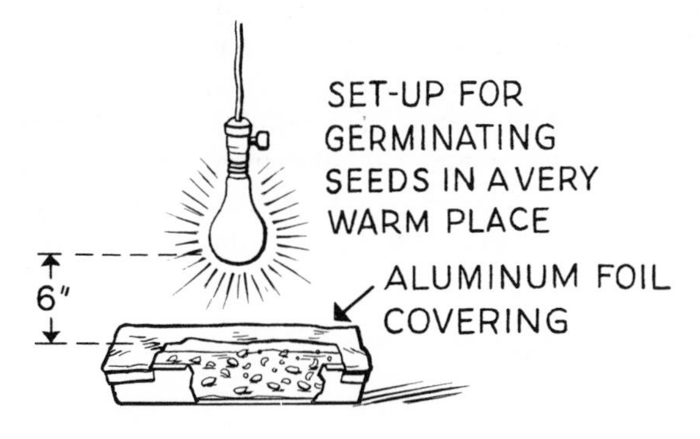

Ten days after starting the experiment, open the germination set-ups. Count the number of seedlings of each kind of seed. Put the results in the following table. Wrap the bulb of a thermometer with aluminum foil. Use this thermometer to find the temperature in the refrigerator and the places where the second and third set-ups were.

	Germination Condition		
	Low	Medium	High
Measured Temperature (°F or °C)			
Number of seeds growing of each kind:			
1.			
2.			
3.			

Use your knowledge of respiration and plant growth to figure out how heat affects the growth of seeds. Can you see why some seeds would not germinate and grow in cold or hot countries or during hot or cold seasons of the year? Do all seeds and plants grow poorly at high temperatures?

3. Will salt help plants grow? Get five waxed-paper drinking cups. Punch one hole in the bottom of each cup; cover the hole with a piece of paper inside the cup. Nearly fill each cup with clean, washed sand. Soak 50 seeds of tomato, bean, corn, or pea in a glass of water for an hour. Now plant 10 soaked seeds in each cup of sand; space the seeds equally, and plant each seed about 1/4 inch below the surface. Label the cups 1, 2, 3, 4, and 5. Put the five cups on a tray in a warm, lighted place, but not in direct sunlight.

Next get five empty quart milk cartons or bottles. Label these 1, 2, 3, 4, and 5. Put a quart of water in each container. Then do the following:

Carton #1. Do not add anything.

Carton #2. Dissolve 1/2 teaspoon of table salt in the water.

Carton #3. Dissolve 1 teaspoon of table salt in the water.

Carton #4. Dissolve 2 teaspoons of table salt in the water.

Carton #5. Dissolve 4 teaspoons of table salt in the water.

Every two days after planting the seeds, water cup #1 with solution from carton #1; water cup #2 with solution from carton #2; and so on with cups 3, 4, and 5. Always add enough solution so that water comes out the bottom of each cup. If you run out of any of the salt solutions, you will need to make some more.

Date	Age of Plant	Treatment—Amount of Salt Added				
		Cup #1 No salt	Cup #2 ½ Teaspoon of salt	Cup #3 1 Teaspoon of salt	Cup #4 2 Teaspoons of salt	Cup #5 4 Teaspoons of salt
	Days	Height of Plants in Inches or Centimeters				
1.	0	0	0	0	0	0
2.	4					
3.	8					
4.	12					
5.	16					
6.	20					

Every four days find the height of every plant in each cup. Measure the height from the sand surface to the top part of each plant. Record the heights in the table. Twenty days after planting the seeds, carefully wash the plants out of each pot and look at the roots. Can you see any effects of the different amounts of salt on the growth of roots?

Figure out the average height of plants in each pot at each age; do this by adding together all the heights of plants of the same age in a pot, and then divide this total by the number of plants in that pot.

Draw a graph of your results. Draw five curves on the same graph; one curve for the average height of plants in each salt treatment. Label each curve #1, 2, 3, 4 or 5. Use the graph on page 117.

Are the five curves the same shape? Did any of the plants look flabby and wilted, as if they weren't getting enough water? Did these plants grow very well? Can you explain the different amount of growth of plants in each salt treatment?

Are there some soils in the United States and the world that are too salty for plants to grow in? When soils are irrigated year after year, do the soils get salty? How can salt be taken out of a soil? Could the growth of plants be slowed down by giving them too much fertilizer?

Try this experiment again using different kinds of plants. Tomato, spinach, sugar beet, carrot, alfalfa, lettuce, and flowers of various kinds all work fine. You will be surprised at how much, or how little, salt these plants can stand.

4. Watching plants change. Mark an area in a patch of weeds like the one talked about in the adventure. The area should be at least a yard or meter square. Put wooden stakes in each corner of the area; stretch heavy strings between the stakes to form an outline of the area. (See illustration on page 106.)

Keep notes in your notebook about the number and kinds of plants that grow in the staked area. Include notes about activities of ants, insects, or other animals in the staked area. If you have a camera, take a picture once a week during your study of the one-meter square plot. The pictures will make a nice display of your study and findings. Keep observing the changes in the weed patch for several months. Record data on rainfall, amount of cloudiness, frosts, temperature, and other things that affect plants. See if you can account for the growth, flowering, and death of plants at different times on the basis of the surroundings of each plant.

ADVENTURE 12

New Words And How To Pronounce Them

VOCABULARY

Accent parts of each word that are in *italics*

aerobic air-*ob*-ik
alcohol *al*-ko-hall
alga (sing.) *al*-ga
algae (pl.) *al*-gee
anaerobic an-air-*ob*-ik
anther *an*-thur
antibiotic *an*-ti-bi-*ot*-ik
Aspergillus As-per-*jil*-us
atom *at*-um
auxin *awx*-in
bacilli (pl.) ba-*sil*-i
bacillus (sing.) ba-*sil*-us
bacteria (pl.) bak-*tear*-ee-a
bacterium (sing.) bak-*tear*-ee-um
biochemist bi-o-*kem*-ist
borate *bor*-ate
botanist *bot*-an-ist
botany *bot*-an-ee
butyric acid byou-*tear*-ik-*ass*-id
calcium *kal*-see-um
calorie *kal*-o-ree
calorimeter *kal*-o-*rim*-eh-tur
cambium *kam*-bee-um
capsule *kap*-sul
carbon dioxide *kar*-bun di-*ok*-side
carotene *kair*-o-tin
catalase *kat*-a-lay-s
Celsius *sell*-see-us
centigrade *sen*-ti-grade
centimeter *sen*-ti-*mee*-tur
chloride *klo*-ride
chlorophyll *klo*-ro-fill
chloroplast *klo*-ro-plast (as in "plaster")
chromatogram kro-*mat*-o-gram
chromatograph kro-*mat*-o-graf
chromatography *krom*-a-*tog*-ra-fee
chromosome *kro*-mo-som
(rhymes with "home")
cocci (pl.) *kok*-see
coccus (sing.) *kok*-us
cone kown (as in "own")
copper *kop*-ur
cotyledon *kot*-eh-*lee*-dun
cytoplasm *si*-toe-plaz-m
deficiency symptoms dee-fish-ens-see *simp*-tums
deoxyribonucleic acid (DNA) dee-*ok*-zee-*ri*-bo-nuk-*lay*-ik *ass*-id
descendant dee-*sen*-dant
diatom *di*-a-tom
dominance *dom*-eh-nans
ecology ee-*kahl*-o-gee
embryo *em*-bree-o
enzyme en-zim (rhymes with "time")
evaporation ee-*vap*-o-*ray*-shun
Fahrenheit *far*-en-hi-t (rhymes with "kite")
female *fee*-mail
fertilization *fur*-till-i-*zay*-shun
filament *fill*-a-ment
fossil *foss*'l
funiculus fu-*nik*-u-lus
gene Jean
generation *jen*-er-*a*-shun
gravitational *grav*-eh-*tay*-shun-uhl
heredity heh-*red*-eh-tee
hilum *hi*-lum
hybrid *hi*-brid
hydrogen *hi*-dro-jin
inherit in-*hair*-it
kilocalorie *kill*-o-*kal*-o-ree
lichen *lie*-ken
magnesium mag-*nee*-zee-um
male mail
manganese *mang*-ga-neez
mastodon *mas*-toe-don
meter *mee*-tur
micron *mi*-kron
mineral *min*-ur-uhl
molecule *mol*-eh-kyou-l
mutation mew-*tay*-shun

nuclei (pl.) *nu*-klee-i
nucleus (sing.) *nu*-klee-us
nutrient *new*-tree-ent
Oedogonium *Ee*-do-*go*-nium
ovary *o*-va-ree
ovule *o*-vyou-l
oxygen *ok*-seh-jen
paleontologist *pay*-lee-on-*tol*-o-jist
parasite *pair*-a-site (rhymes with "mite")
penicillin *pen*-eh-*sil*-in
Penicillium *Pen*-eh-*sil*-ee-um
peroxide pur-*ok*-side
petal *peh*-tul
petiole *pet*-ee-ohl
phloem *flo*-em
phosphate *foss*-fate
phosphorus *foss*-for-us
photosynthesis *fo*-to-*sin*-thee-sis
pigment *pig*-ment
pistil *pis*-t'l
placenta pla-*sent*-a
pollen *pahl*-en
pollination *pahl*-en-*nay*-shun
potassium po-*tass*-ee-um
potometer po-*tom*-eh-tur
recessive ree-*ses*-iv
reproduction *ree*-pro-*duk*-shun
respiration *res*-peh-*ray*-shun
rhizoid *ri*-zoid
Rhizopus *Ri*-zo-pus
sepal *see*-pull
saprophyte *sap*-ro-fite (rhymes with "kite")
sperm spurm
Sphagnum *sfag*-num
spindle *spin*-d'l
spirillum spi-*ril*-um
Spirogyra *Spi*-ro-*ji*-ra
spore spor
stamen *stay*-men
starch *star*-ch
sterile *stair*-ill
stigma *stig*-ma
stomate *sto*-mate
style *sti*-l (rhymes with "mile")
sulfate *sul*-fate
transpiration *tran*-spi-*ray*-shun
vacuole *vak*-u-uhl
vein vain
xanthophyll *zan*-tho-fill
xylem zi-lem (as in "xylophone")
yeast *yee*-st
zinc zingk

INDEX

Pages in *italics* have pictures.

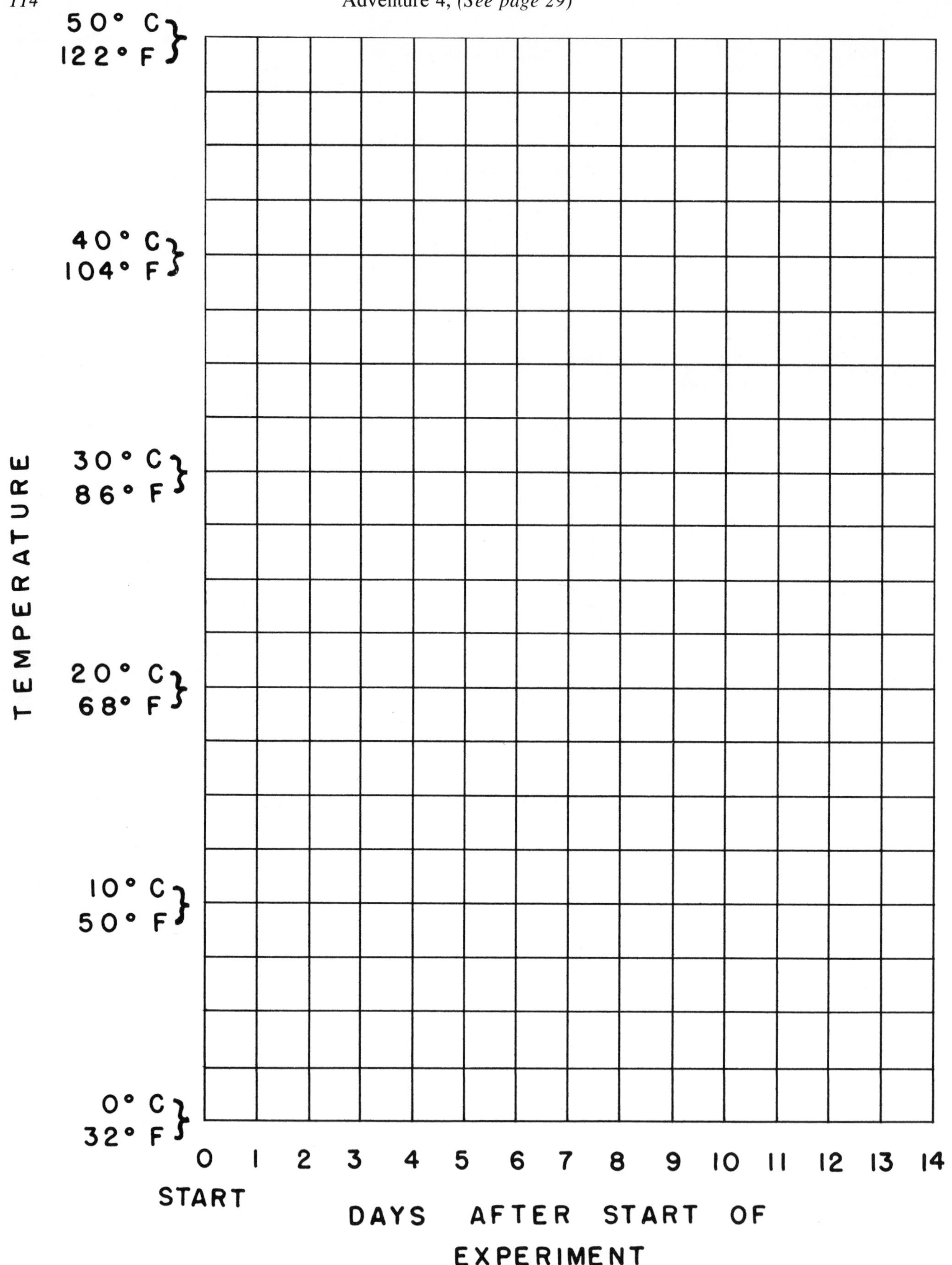

50° C
122° F
40° C
104° F
30° C
86° F
20° C
68° F
10° C
50° F
0° C
32° F
TEMPERATURE
0 1 2 3 4 5 6 7 8 9 10 11 12 13 14
START
DAYS AFTER START OF EXPERIMENT

Adventure 5
(See page 41)

AVERAGE HEIGHT (CENTIMETERS OR INCHES) OF PLANTS IN EACH POT

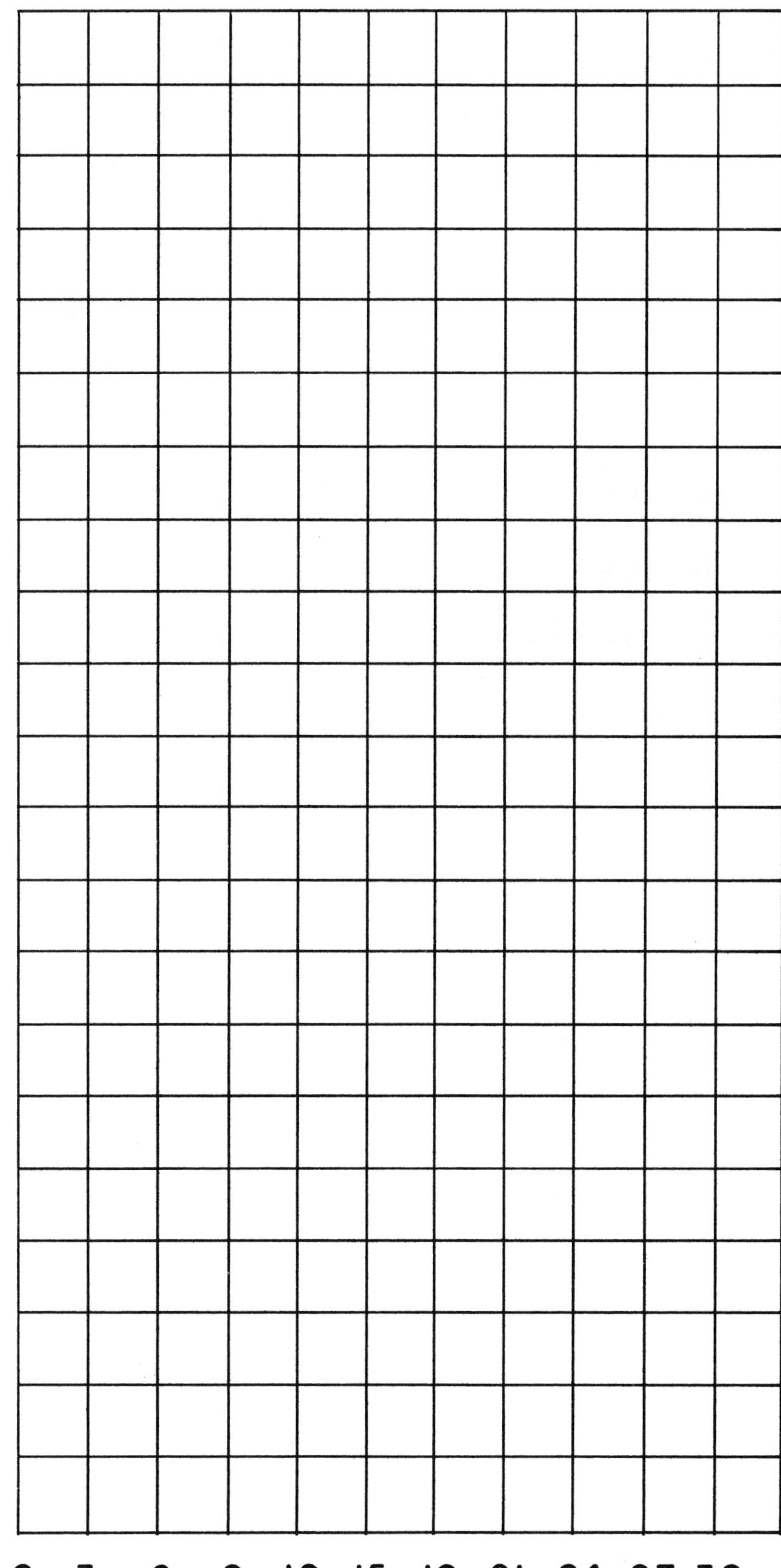

DAYS AFTER BEGINNING TREATMENTS

Adventure 7
(See page 62)

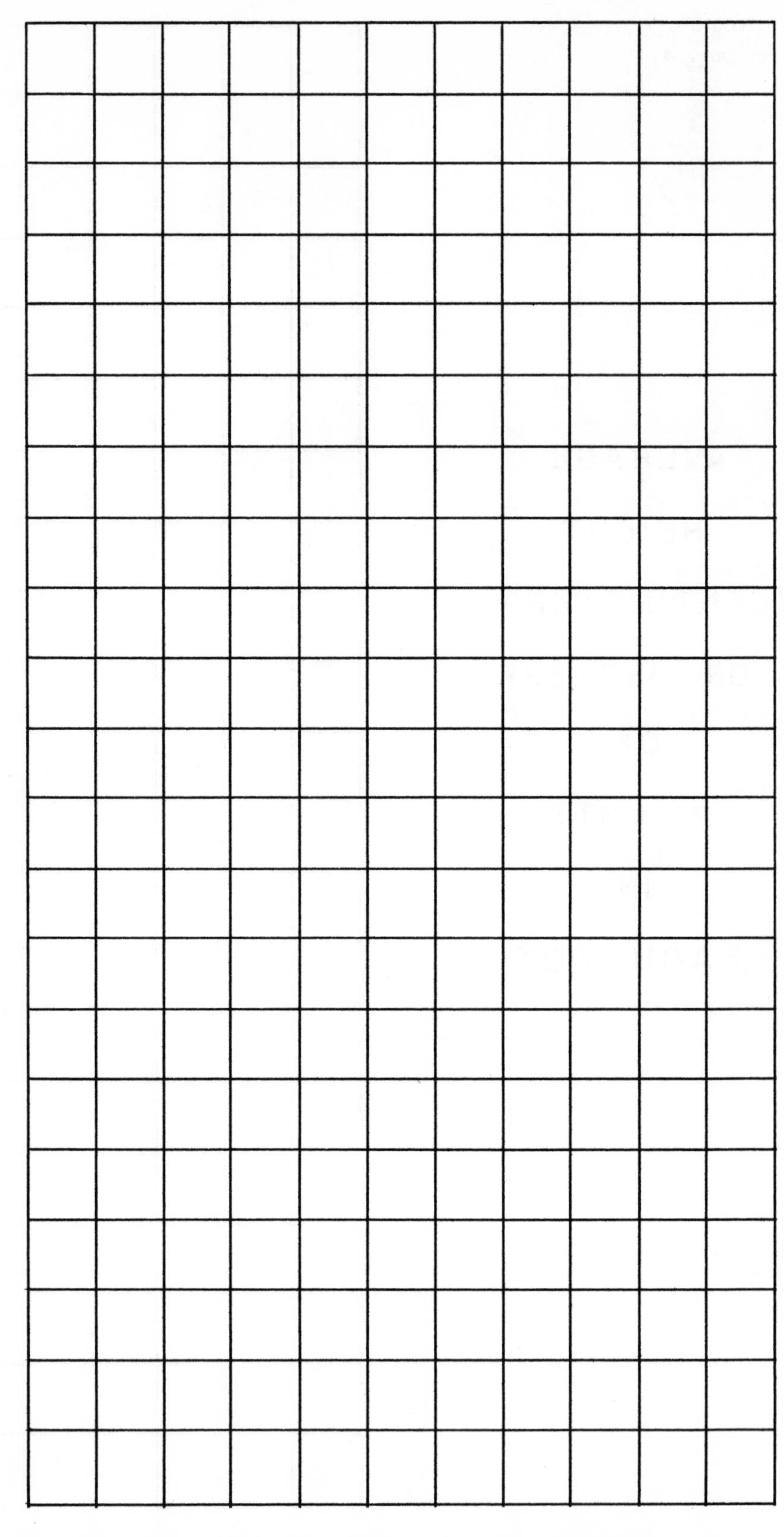

Adventure 11
(See page 110)

AVERAGE HEIGHT (CENTIMETERS OR INCHES) OF PLANTS IN EACH CUP

0

0 4 8 12 16 20 24

AGE OF PLANTS, IN DAYS

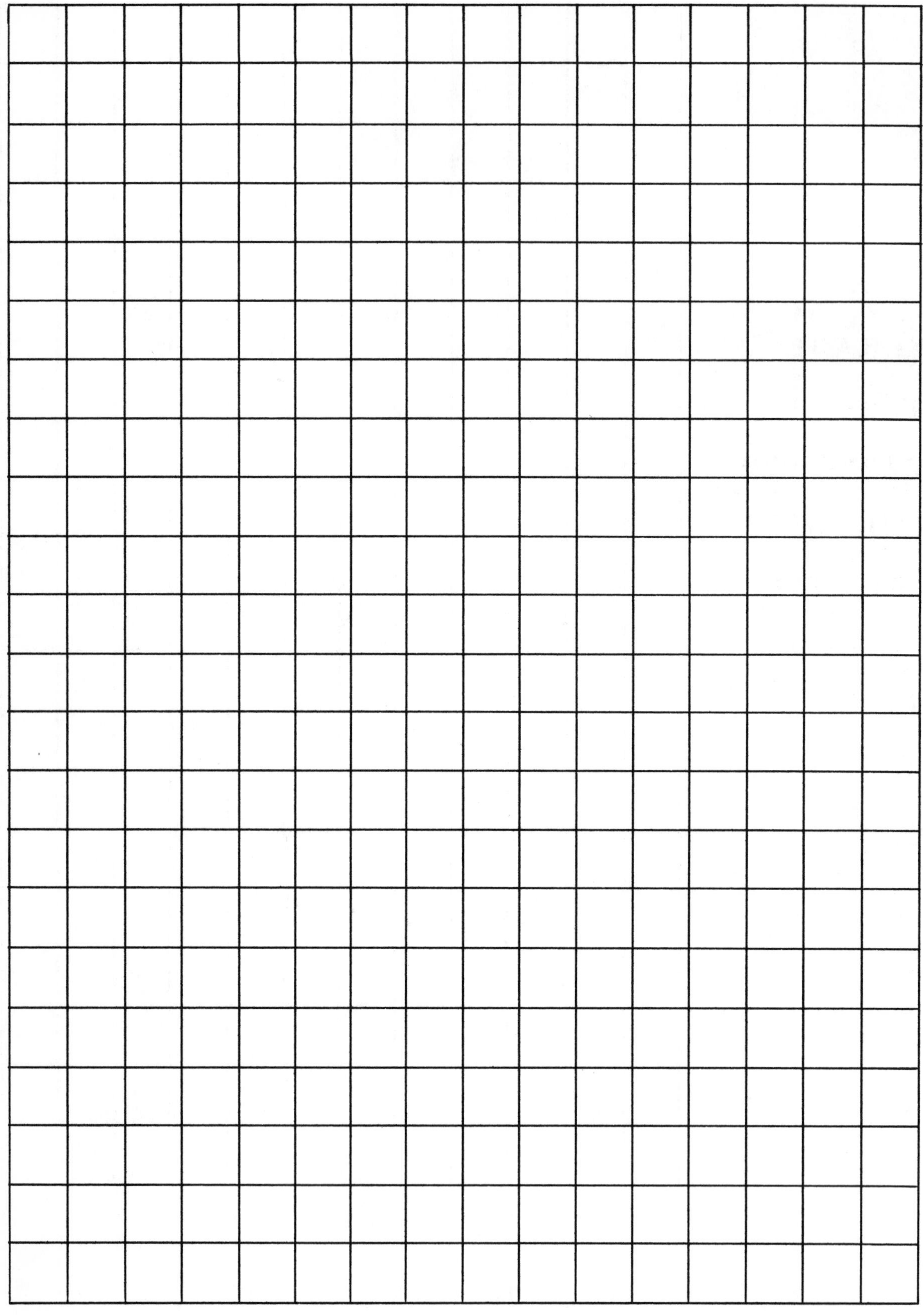
0
0

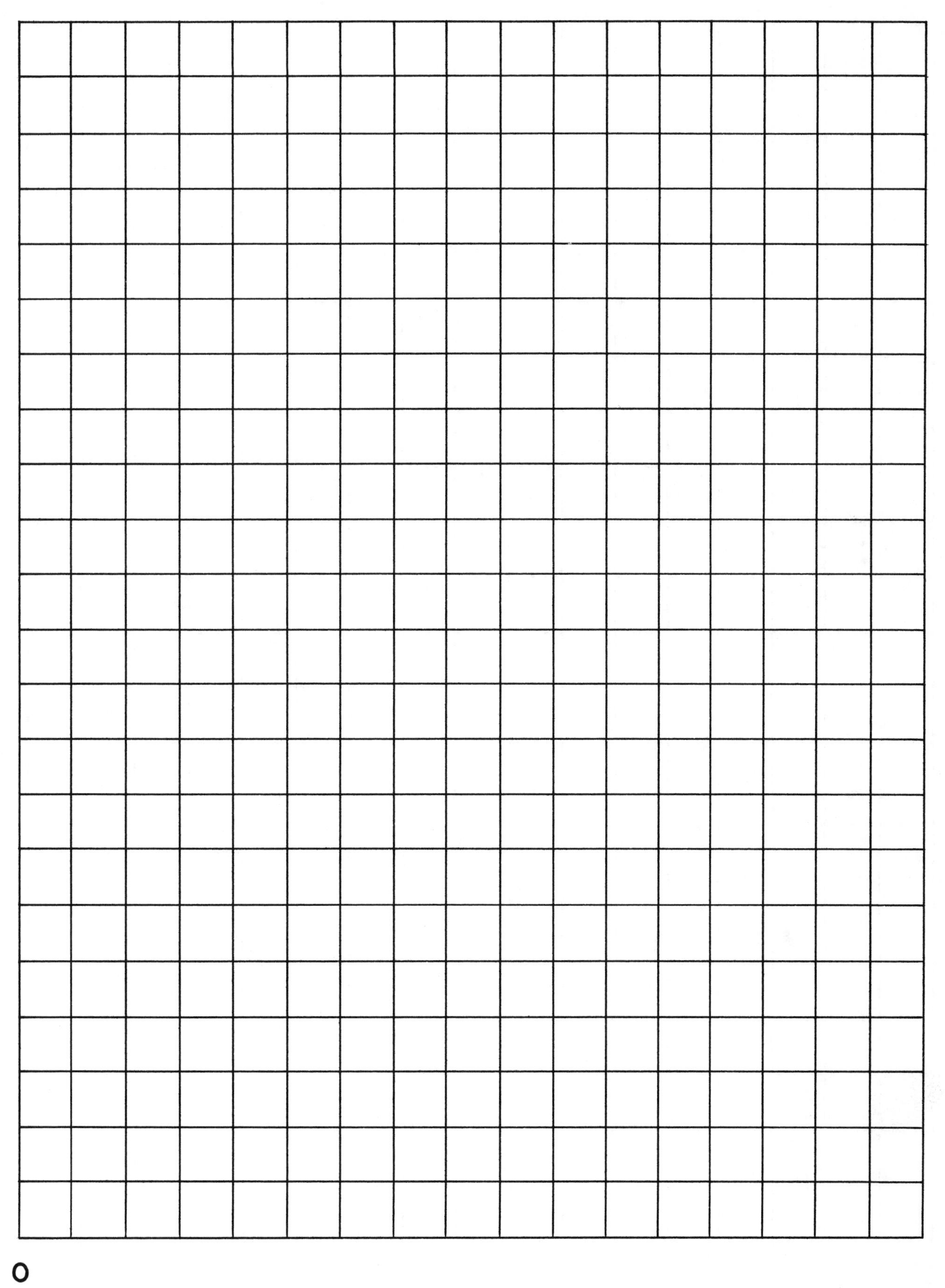

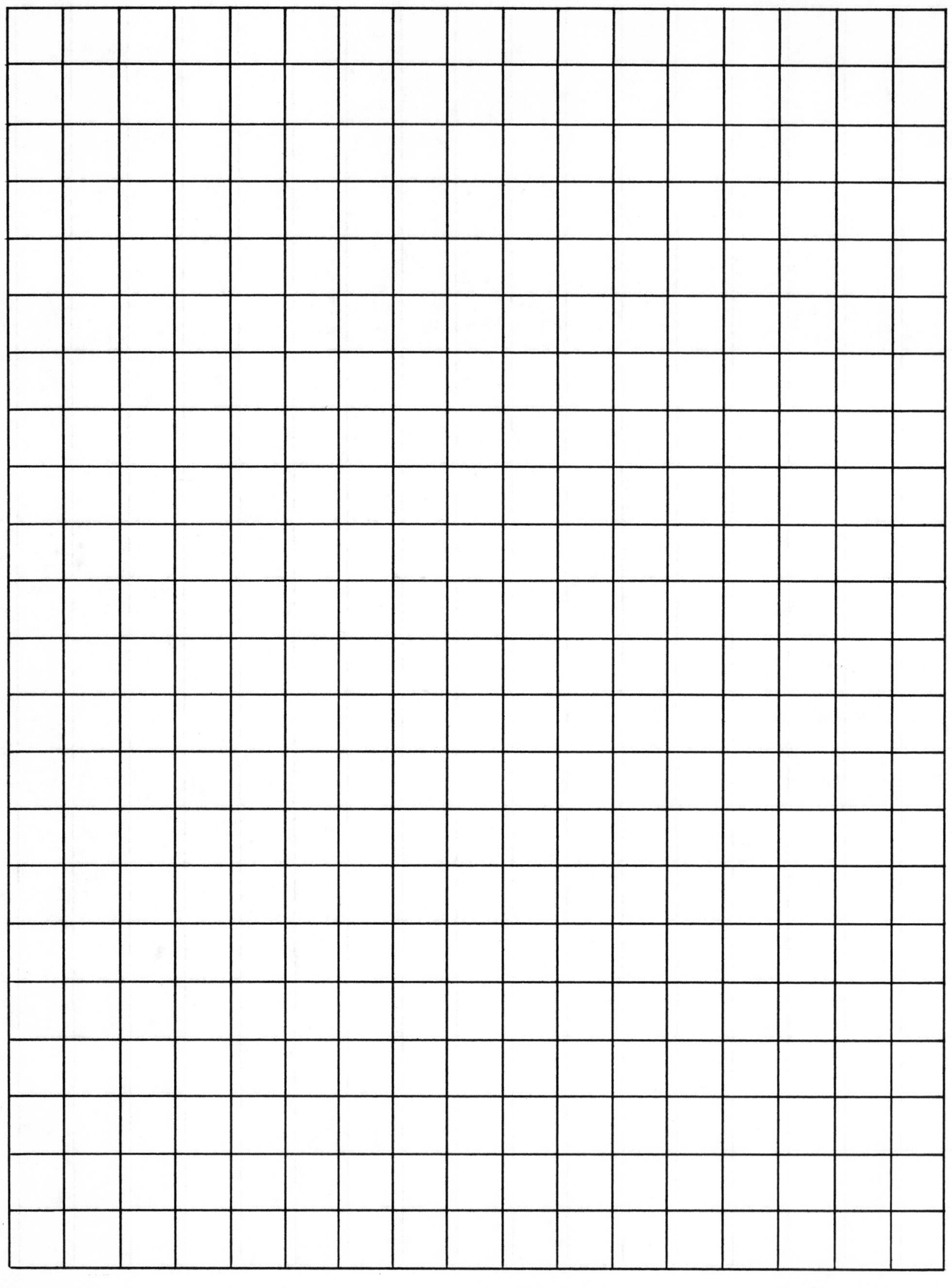

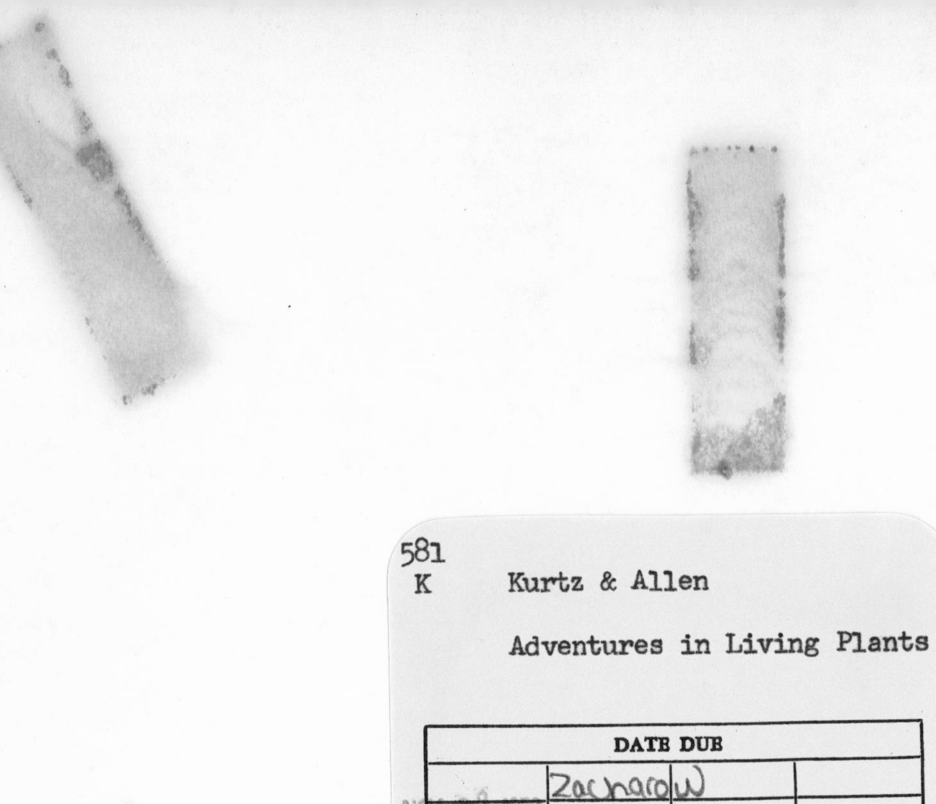

Kurtz & Allen

Adventures in Living Plants

DATE DUE			
NOV 2? 1979	Zacharow		
GAYLORD M-2			PRINTED IN U.S.A.